CORYD

CATFISH

An Aquarist's Handbook

Derek Lambourne

Series Editor: Derek Lambert

BLANDFORD

A Blandford Book
First published in the UK 1995
by Blandford
(a Cassell imprint)
Wellington House
125 Strand
London WC2R 0BB

Distributed in the United States
by Sterling Publishing Co., Inc.
387 Park Avenue South, New York, NY 10016–8810

Distributed in Australia
by Capricorn Link (Australia) Pty Ltd
2/13 Carrington Road, Castle Hill, NSW 2154

*A catalogue record for this book is available from
the British Library*

ISBN 0 7137 2367 X

Typeset by Cambrian Typesetters, Frimley, Surrey
Printed and bound in Spain

Contents

Acknowledgements

Thanks are due to: Roy Goodson, who all those years ago persuaded me that I could get people interested in catfish; Gordon Howes of the Natural History Museum, who encouraged my interest in catfish; and Drs Nijssen and Isbrücker of the University of Amsterdam, who gave up a great deal of their time to sorting out our queries and identification problems on this group of fish.

Special thanks to: Ian Fuller for all his excellent line drawings of young *Corydoras* and all the information on breeding – I have known Ian since my early fish-keeping days and his knowledge on keeping and breeding *Corydoras* is second to none; Roy Davis, for all his help and encouragement, and for supplying me, over the years, with many a fine catfish specimen. I must also thank all my friends (far too numerous to mention) for allowing me to photograph their fish. Finally, I must thank my wife Pat for all her support and for typing the manuscript, for without her this book would probably never have been written.

PICTURE CREDITS

Colour Photographs
Ian Fuller: p. 107 (middle).

Line Drawings
Ian Fuller: pp. 50, 55, 66, 70, 74, 76, 78, 91, 93, 95, 102, 106, 121
Martin Rooney: p. 73 (lower three).

All other photographs and drawings are by the author.

Foreword

Some 20 years ago, the keeping of exotic catfish in aquariums was virtually unheard of and only a few species of *Corydoras*, *Plecostomus* and *Synodontis* were available. Nowadays, catfish aquatics is a specialist branch of aquarium-keeping; catfish species are being exhibited at their 'own' shows and information about them is being disseminated through the magazines and meetings of catfish societies and groups. Similarly, scientific interest in catfish has been activated in recent years, particularly amongst ichthyologists in Brazil, Venezuela and the USA. There are now few families of catfish which are not being actively studied by somebody somewhere. The surge of interest in catfishes, at both aquarium and scientific levels, has in no small part been due to the founding of the Catfish Association of Great Britain, of which the author of this book (and his wife Pat) were founder members. Their enthusiasm for their subjects and their thirst for knowledge has, over these past years, been unflagging and is realized in this book.

Corydoras has been the most popular of all aquarium-kept catfish, the breeding behaviour of some species having been well documented by aquarists. There are probably more species of *Corydoras* than have been described for any other catfish genus. Most are recognizable by their colour pattern, which in some is very distinctive but in others tends to be variable and hence makes identification problematical. In the latter cases, it is very difficult to determine whether one is dealing with a single, geographically-widespread, variable species or several distinct ones. Derek Lambourne has done an excellent job and has produced an indispensable work for all *Corydoras* lovers.

Gordon J. Howes
Fish Section
Natural History Museum

Preface

Over the last 40 years or so, the aquarium hobby has made valuable observations on the biology of fish, and of catfish in particular. This has become even more evident over the last 20 years. Once these observations have been sorted out and classified, they will form an essential part of our knowledge of this fascinating group of fish and could also become a foundation and incentive for further developments.

I think it can fairly be said that many discoveries of modern biological research have come about by ichthyologists following up aquarists' observations. Due to scientific advances, attitudes of aquarists have undergone changes and this has undoubtedly led them more towards scientific research.

Over 25 years ago, my wife and I began our interest in catfish – not just *Corydoras*, but all species of catfish. We scoured the shops for different species and often, when we found a fish that we liked, the shop-owner did not know what the fish was called and, in many cases, even what continent it came from. Because of this, we decided that not enough was known about catfish and we thought we should try to do something about it.

In 1973, along with 3 other friends, we founded the Catfish Association of Great Britain. We contacted the staff of the Fish Section of the Natural History Museum and they agreed to help us as much as they could. Gordon Howes, who worked in this section, gave us an enormous amount of help and information and, through his influence, we also managed to coerce Drs H. Greenwood and K. Banister into helping as well. Eventually, when we wanted to find out more about *Corydoras*, Gordon Howes recommended that we contact the University of Amsterdam, where work on the genus *Corydoras* was in progress. We took his advice and contacted Drs Nijssen and Isbrücker, and thus our long and enjoyable association with the University of Amsterdam began. Since then Drs Nijssen and Isbrücker have given us a great deal of their time and information. Much of what is known today about catfish is due to the efforts of the Catfish Association and to its publications.

Information on catfish has gone from strength to strength over the last 10 years or so and many different publications are now issued. Most are very informative, with some excellent pictures of fish that we rarely see and, indeed, some that we are not likely to see.

Many fish habitats are gradually disappearing in the wild and less fish will be imported in future. Indeed, there are already export restrictions on some species by several countries. Thousands of fish die before they even get to our aquariums, due to poor conditions at some of the holding stations (usually caused by overcrowding and water pollution). Many *Corydoras* are now being bred in captivity, so perhaps it is up to us, the aquarists, to keep the species going.

The object of this book is to share with you the knowledge I have accumulated over many years on this fascinating group of catfish.

Any reader who wants to contact me to either agree or disagree with anything I have said will be most welcome to do so. Any letters addressed to the Publisher will find me and be assured of an answer.

I do hope that you will find at least *one* thing in this publication that perhaps is new to you.

Derek Lambourne

Introduction

It is hoped that this handbook will give you some of the information that you are looking for. It is not intended for the complete beginner but for everyone interested in keeping, breeding and learning a little more about the genus *Corydoras*.

Most of the information on the distribution of these fish comes from the papers written by Drs Nijssen and Isbrücker of the University of Amsterdam. In 1980 they undertook a revision of the genus *Corydoras*. People asking me about this revision have assumed that Drs Nijssen and Isbrücker just read everything other people had written about earlier described specimens and then reprinted it. This is not so; they had to call in all the type specimens of *Corydoras* from at least 22 different museum collections around the world and set about checking them all out. Naturally, after being preserved for so long, some specimens were in very poor condition – their distinguishing pigment was almost non-existent – so this made their task even more difficult. Some specimens had even been lost due to the 2 World Wars – so they had to set about redescribing them, no easy thing to do. Still, at the end of their mammoth task, we have up-to-date information on this group of fish.

Unfortunately the hobby literature published on *Corydoras* has not had the benefit of such a major revision. Misidentified photographs and inaccurate descriptions abound, as do incorrectly-identified fish within the trade. To avoid misleading the reader further, I have only included descriptions and photographs of fish which have been accurately identified. I have also omitted descriptions of fish that are only known from preserved material as these may bear little resemblance to the living animal.

New species are being discovered and described almost yearly so, by the time this book is published, there will probably be more species to add to the list. The information given in the list of *Corydoras* species in Chapter 9 was up to date as of September 1992. The taxonomic details include synonyms of those fish that have been known by other names and also the etymology of the species name where this is known.

An '-i' or '-ii' ending to a specific name indicates that the fish concerned has been named after a man; an '-ae' ending indicates that it has been named after a woman. For example, *C. blochi blochi* Nijssen, 1971, was named in honour of Dr Bloch, a famous German ichthyologist, and *C. evelynae* Rössel, 1963, was named after Mrs Evelyn Axelrod.

Species' names derived from the locality in which they were collected (country, city, river etc.) are formed from the name of that locality followed by the ending '-ensis', e.g. *C. guianensis* Nijssen, 1970 (from the Guiana countries), *C. surinamensis* (from Surinam) and *C. potaroensis* (from the Potaro River).

Details of distribution have been taken from the scientific literature. Scientific expeditions always record the location where they collect their specimens, but not every fish-collector records the exact location. Therefore, the distribution of some species is much wider than is recorded.

Descriptions are given for most species (this was not always possible for the less well-known *Corydoras*) and the size of the largest specimen examined and the size that the fish could be expected to reach in the aquarium. All sizes quoted are standard length (SL).

The section on breeding will tell you whether or not the fish have been bred under aquarium conditions, and whether any sexual differences are known. Line drawings of the juvenile *Corydoras* have been included to show how different the young fish look from the adults at differing stages in their development. *Corydoras* breed in several different ways, depending on the species, and I have tried to cover all that is known.

Some *Corydoras* species have an extremely variable colour pattern and, where possible, I have tried to illustrate the average within that species.

When you first begin to keep *Corydoras*, the first names that you will hear are *C. julii* Steindachner, 1906, and C. punctatus (Bloch, 1794). I have been a keen aquarist for almost 30 years and have never seen live specimens of either of these fish (although I have seen preserved specimens of both in a museum). When I have seen fish advertised as *C. julii*, they invariably turn out to be *C. trilineatus* Cope, 1872, or *C. leopardus* Myers, 1933. In the case of *C. punctatus*, it seems that any *Corydoras* with spots on the body is so named and thus it could be any one of a number of different species, but never the true *C. punctatus*.

Corydoras can live for many years. I have kept a few species that have lived for 15 years and I know of one fish – a *Corydoras aeneus* (Gill, 1858) – that was 34 years old. Because of their longevity, these fish can be particularly rewarding to keep.

1
Classification

Catfish belong to the order of freshwater fish named Cypriniformes. One of the distinguishing features of this order is the presence of a structure called the Weberian apparatus (see p. 17).

Catfish, although generally bottom-dwellers, have evolved a bewildering diversity of shapes, anatomical structures and strange habits. In the genus *Synodontis*, for instance, some species swim inverted beneath the surface of the water, whereas *Malapterurus electricus* uses its electric discharge to ward off predators and stun prey-animals. Another catfish (*Vandellia*) has evolved into a parasite. This great variety of form, of which the above-mentioned is but a small example, has led to the catfish being classified into about 30 families. Two of these, the Ariidae and the Plotosidae, have reverted back to a marine existence. Of the remainder, there are 14 families endemic to South America, 8 in Asia, 3 in Africa and 1 each in Europe and North America.

Callichthyidae

The family Callichthyidae includes probably the best known of aquarium catfish and contains 6 genera: *Aspidoras*, *Brochis*, *Callichthys*, *Corydoras*, *Dianema* and *Hoplosternum*. Since *Aspidoras* and *Brochis* are similar to *Corydoras* in body form, I shall briefly deal with these 2 genera before moving on to *Corydoras*.

Aspidoras

In general, *Aspidoras* are smaller and more slender than *Corydoras* and can be easily distinguished from all other members of the callichthyid genera by the possession of 2 cranial fontanels (see Chapter 2, Fig. 1). The frontal fontanel (round or slightly oval in shape) always penetrates the roof of the skull whereas the posterior fontanel is closed in adult specimens, leaving a small, roundish, shallow pit.

Four hundred specimens of 13 different species of *Aspidoras* were examined by Nijssen and Isbrücker. In all specimens, a basically-similar structure of the skull roof was found. No other callichthyids showed this structure and no intermediate structure was found in over 100 species of the related genus *Corydoras*. *Corydoras*, *Brochis* and *Dianema* possess a single open fontanel, much larger and more elongate than the frontal fontanel in *Aspidoras*.

All 14 species that have been described come from Brazil. They are:

A. albater Nijssen & Isbrücker, 1976
A. brunneus Nijssen & Isbrücker, 1976
A. carvalhoi Nijssen & Isbrücker, 1976
A. eurycephalus Nijssen & Isbrücker, 1976
A. fascoguttatus Nijssen & Isbrücker, 1976
A. lakoi P. de Miranda Ribeiro, 1949
A. maculosus Nijssen & Isbrücker, 1976
A. menezesi Nijssen & Isbrücker, 1976
A. pauciradiatus (Weitzman & Nijssen, 1970)
A. poecilus Nijssen & Isbrücker, 1976
A. raimundi (Steindachner, 1907)
A. rochai R. Von Ihering, 1907
A. spilotus Nijssen & Isbrücker, 1976
A. virgulatus Nijssen & Isbrücker, 1976

Brochis

Brochis differ from *Corydoras* in having more dorsal fin rays. In *Brochis* there are 10–18, whilst *Corydoras* has 6–8. *Brochis* also have a deeper body than most species of *Corydoras*.

There are 3 known species of *Brochis*:

B. britskii Nijssen & Isbrücker, 1983   This species was described from specimens collected in the Mato Grosso in Brazil. It has 15–18 dorsal fin rays and the largest specimen examined was 78.6 mm long.

B. multiradiatus (Orces Villagomez, 1960)   This species is found in Brazil, Ecuador and Peru. It has 15–17 dorsal fin rays and the largest specimen examined was 79.7 mm long.

B. splendens (Castelnau, 1855)   This species is also found in Brazil, Ecuador and Peru. It has 10–12 dorsal fin rays and the largest specimen examined was 62.8 mm long.

Corydoras

Corydoras (with over 120 species) are possibly the best known of any aquarium catfish. A number of studies have been undertaken on this genus. These have covered anatomy, physiology and systematics. A major revision of the genus was undertaken by Nijssen and Isbrücker in 1980.

Although, for the most part, the families of catfish can be distinguished from one another on good anatomical features, the situation becomes less easy at low taxonomic (classificatory) levels. The most difficult problems for the ichthyologist arise at the species level. In earlier times, when catfish were first being studied, relatively few specimens were available and it was comparatively easy to distinguish one form or 'species' from another. In these days, with far larger samples available, we are now aware that many 'species' are probably only examples of population variation within a single species. This is one reason for the name-changing by taxonomists that so often irritates aquarists; e.g. a fish that was known as *C. funnelli* Fraser Brunner, 1947, for many years turned out to be *C. leopardus* Myers, 1933. When you have known a fish by one name for a long time, it can be very difficult to accept the new name.

Problems in Classification

One of the major problems for the ichthyologist is to work out the inter-relationships of catfish, i.e. to try and discover their phylogeny (or evolutionary history). There are few fossils of catfish and those that do exist tell very little about the evolution of the group. By studying the comparative anatomy of living catfish, it is possible to recognize certain features as indicating a common ancestry and so to work out their family trees. However, this method of study is painstaking and requires detailed examination of specimens representing several hundred genera before a satisfactory 'natural' classification can be achieved.

When a zoologist is asked to 'classify' a fish, the enquirer invariably means him to 'identify' it. Classification, as noted above, is the ordering of species into a scheme which ultimately reflects their evolutionary history. Identification is simply applying a name to a specimen. More often than not, in the case of catfish, the specimens will be of a known species. Usually it is essential to know the locality where the fish was found, so that a checklist of the fishes of that area can be consulted. In some cases a revision, or monograph, of a particular family is available which contains identification keys for species or species-groups. Finally, if identification proves particularly difficult, direct comparison can be made between the unknown fish and preserved specimens of known species. One fish immediately springs to mind here. A *Corydoras* that had been coming into the UK for a year or so could not be identified. It did not match up with any of the specimens at the museums so a couple of dead specimens were sent to Amsterdam University for identification. This took some time, but finally the specimens were identified as *C. habrosus* Weitzman, 1960. The preserved specimens of *C. habrosus* had faded so much that comparisons had proved very difficult. In the case of catfish, many species are known from single specimens and so identification cannot be achieved with certainty.

One other difficulty confronting the ichthyologist is the lack of knowledge concerning variability within a species. Indeed, in the past, it has been known for 'species' to be described on the basis of juveniles or sexual differences. This was the case with *C. myersi* P. de Miranda Ribeiro, 1942. *C. myersi* was described as a new species but, on later examination, it was found to be an adult specimen of *C. rabauti* La Monte, 1941, which had been described from 7 preserved specimens and from 3, living, juvenile aquarium specimens measuring 13.7–17.4 mm. Only by having large samples of growth stages, from widespread geographic areas, can this variability be recognized.

Nomenclature

As mentioned previously, the species is the lowest taxonomic category and, indeed, is the only 'true' biological one, i.e. the species is recognized as the entity upon which natural selection (the process of evolution) operates. This is a rather simplistic view of the species concept which, in practice, is much more complex because a species may comprise several populations. There is much argument and discussion amongst biologists as to what a species actually is and, indeed, what 'natural selection' means – but such technical problems do not concern us here.

All higher-level categories are man-made and, although having a biological basis, are of classificatory convenience. To know the correct name of a fish is of great importance when consulting work already carried out by others. Also, the use of the scientific name by workers of all nationalities permits universal recognition. Referring to a fish as a 'spotted catfish' brings to mind not only *C. punctatus* but also *C. sychri* and *C. atropersonatus*, among others. By using the scientific name of a fish you can be sure that everyone is talking about the same species.

The complete species name is referred to as a *binomen*, and is comprised of the generic name and the specific (species or trivial) name. It is customary to add the name of the author of the species and the date of publication, e.g. *C. metae* Eigenmann, 1914. Brackets around the author's name, e.g. *C. aeneus* (Gill, 1858), indicates that, although the original description is accepted, the generic name is no longer valid and has been changed since the species was first described.

2
Anatomy

The life style of *Corydoras* is very much reflected in the anatomy of the fish themselves. The body of most *Corydoras* is flattened on the ventral (lower) surface, a feature typical of organisms which spend most of their lives on the substrate (river bottom).

External Covering

In *Corydoras* the scales common in most fish are replaced by 2 series of bony plates (called lateral scutes) which cover the sides of the fish. These are for protection from the environment, parasites and predators. Much of the head of a *Corydoras* is likewise protected with a series of bony plates. These consist of the intra-orbital bones, pre-operculum, operculum and supra-occipital shield. These bony plates, or *fulcra*, together with tough fin spines located at the front of the dorsal and pectoral fins, which have the ability to lock rigidly away from the body, make *Corydoras* particularly unpalatable prey for most carnivores.

Sensory Organs

The bony plates are pierced by a number of sensory organs. Foremost amongst these is the lateral-line canal, which runs along the flanks of the fish. It contains sensors which help pick up vibrations, so warning the fish of the approach of other animals. The nasal opening is positioned in front of the eye and is an opening to a closed pit covered with organs which are sensitive to smell.

One of the most unusual features of *Corydoras* is that their eyes can be moved independently and, from time to time, they will be rotated in their sockets – apparently to clean them. This peculiar habit has been interpreted by aquarists as 'winking' and is one of the most endearing characteristics of these fish.

Fins

Corydoras have 8 fins, of which 4 are unpaired. These are: the dorsal, which is a medial fin on the top of the back; the caudal, or tail, fin; the anal fin, situated immediately behind the anus, and an additional very small dorsal fin, positioned in front of the caudal fin. This last fin, called

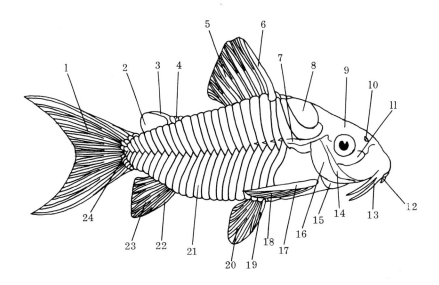

Fig. 1 Anatomy of a *Corydoras* catfish. 1. Caudal fin. 2. Adipose fin. 3. Adipose or second dorsal spine. 4. Pre-adipose plates. 5. Dorsal fin. 6. Dorsal fin spine. 7. Lateral-line canal. 8. Supra-occipital shield. 9. Fontanel. 10. Nasal opening. 11. Intra-orbital bone. 12. Mental barbel 13. Rictal barbel. 14. Pre-operculum. 15. Branchiostegal membrane. 16. Operculum or cleithrum. 17. Pectoral fin spine. 18. Pectoral fin. 19. Pelvic or ventral fin spine. 20. Pelvic or ventral fin. 21. Lateral scutes. 22. Anal fin spine. 23. Anal fin. 24. Caudal peduncle.

the adipose fin, consists of a spiny projection with a membrane attached. The paired pectoral fins are situated laterally and the paired pelvic fins (sometimes referred to as ventral fins) are situated between the pectoral and anal fins.

The pelvic fins are normally just used as stabilizers when a fish swims. However, in female *Corydoras*, these fins play a very important role during breeding. At this time, they are clasped together, forming a pouch into which the eggs are laid before being pushed on to the spawning-site.

Weberian Apparatus

This is a modification of parts of the first 4 vertebrae to form an interconnected chain of bones. These link the swimbladder to the inner ear and function as oscillators to enhance sound and other vibrations.

Corydoras showing barbels in an ideal condition for breeding.

Barbels

These structures (1 pair at the junction of the lips at the corners of the mouth – the rictal barbels, and 1–3 pairs on the lower lip – the mental barbels) are clearly adaptations specifically developed to enhance the *Corydoras*'s success in finding food hidden in the substrate. Apart from finding hidden food particles, the barbels play a vital role during spawning (p. 37). If they become too badly damaged, they may not be able to regenerate, thus putting the fish at a distinct disadvantage in the wild and possibly preventing it from successfully spawning.

3
The Natural Environment

Corydoras are distributed widely in South America, from Brazil, Uruguay and northern Argentina to the Guianas, Venezuela, Colombia and Trinidad. However, it is in the Amazon – the largest river, lake and swamp ecosystem on Earth – that *Corydoras* are said to be found in abundance. This huge wilderness extends across two-fifths of South America, north and south of the equator. It is bisected by the Amazon River and networked by no less than 1,100 tributaries. Most of the region is a flat river basin, less than 200 m above sea level. This area of approximately 6.5 million km^2 is bounded by the Andes in the west and the lower Guyana and Brazilian shields in the north and south. Much of the basin is infertile, and only the parts that are regularly flooded have rich soils. The average depth of the Amazon during flood-times is 30–50 m.

The Amazon is not just a river; it is an integrated system of rivers and jungles taking up about half of Brazil and parts of 8 other South American countries. It is possibly the greatest river in the world, rising as a brook about 5,000 m up in the snow-capped Andes of Peru, just 193 km from the Pacific, plunging down through ravines and gorges, and flowing through the vast basin until it floods into the Atlantic, 6,400 km to the east, on the other side of the continent.

It is also possibly the second longest river in the world (after the Nile) but, by volume alone, the Amazon is unrivalled. The middle and upper reaches have tributaries with many cataracts and waterfalls, and their waters are relatively clear and soft, but nowadays they contain a great deal of mercury, a by-product of the gold-mining operations.

The Amazonian lowlands are mainly blackwater rivers and their waters are dark, yet clean. The sandy soil of the Amazon basin is very poor in nutrients and, chemically, the water resembles distilled water. Despite this, many rivers are dark in colour – the most famous being the Rio Negro, where the water is the colour of strong tea.

The characins, catfish and electric knife-fish account for over 80 per cent of the 3,000 (approximately) fish species of the Amazon, the richest ichthyological region in the world. The diversity of the environment has provided the stimulus for catfish to evolve various anatomical features to best suit particular habitats. The thick scutes of callichthyids, doradids and loricariids act not only as a protective shield against predators but also against abrasion in fast-flowing waters.

Corydoras usually inhabit slowly-moving streams and rivers where the water is shallow (no more than 2 m in Surinam according to Nijssen) and very clear. Some *Corydoras* prefer sandy bottoms, but the substrate varies from region to region; in some places it will be covered with dead leaves and in others mixed with mud. The banks and sides of the rivers and streams are often covered with a lush growth of plants.

With such a widespread distribution, *Corydoras* inhabit a wide variety of water types and temperatures. They generally seem to prefer soft, neutral to slightly acid waters (in Surinam waters of pH 5.3–6.7) and a hardness of 5–10°dH. Nevertheless, *C. barbatus* and *C. macropterus* were collected from a creek in Brazil where the temperature of the water was 18°C, the pH below 4.8 and the water looked like tea. High-altitude species come from water with temperatures as low as 12°C and, in Surinam, *Corydoras* have been collected in waters where the temperature was as high as 32°C. They have a limited tolerance to salt and are not found in areas that are subjected to tidal influences.

It is reported that many species are commonly seen in shoals ranging from hundreds to possibly thousands and consisting of males, females and juveniles. They mainly mill about on the bottom, stirring up silt in their search for food and often burying their snout up to their eyes. In the wild, their main foods are worms, bottom-dwelling insects, insect larvae and some vegetable matter. Occasionally they can also be seen inverted, feeding from the surface, like the African genus *Synodontis*.

Most *Corydoras* are able to survive in less than ideal conditions because of their ability to utilize atmospheric oxygen. In some of the swampy or muddy areas, if the oxygen level in the water becomes very low, they can be seen darting to the surface, where they take air from the atmosphere into their mouth; this then passes through the intestines where the oxygen is extracted. In such situations, if a fish cannot reach the surface for air, it may die of suffocation. This behaviour can be used as an indicator in the home aquarium: if your *Corydoras* are continually dashing to the surface, check the quality of the water in your tank.

In their natural environment, *Corydoras* usually spawn at the beginning of the rainy season (April or May in Surinam). With the rise in water levels, more areas become available for breeding and the rain-water washes an abundance of foods from the land into the rivers.

It is often easy to be misled into thinking that fish collected from the same general region will have the same habitat requirements. Pools of static water and marshy areas are often choked with submerged vegetation, whereas hillstreams often produce turbulent water, rushing over stones or sand, without a plant in sight. Many species survive in aquarium conditions which are often completely different from those in their natural habitat, but they usually acclimatize fairly quickly if they are well looked after. If fish have spawned once, they will usually do so again and again. Naturally, aquarium-bred specimens do not need to be pandered to quite as much as their wild-caught relations.

4
The Aquarium Environment

When setting up an aquarium, it is important to leave it for *at least 1 week* before adding any fish. Thereafter, the best possible conditions must be maintained to ensure the health of your fish.

Water

Naturally, the waters from which your fish are caught are all slightly different in quality. You must remember that, by the time the fish get into your aquarium, they have been subjected to many different water conditions and are often quite distressed. It says much for their hardiness and physical tolerance that, despite all this, they survive very well in a domestic water-supply, which varies greatly in quality from one part of a country to the other.

To keep *Corydoras* healthy in an aquarium environment takes little but regular effort. With many of the *Corydoras* species, soft acid water is needed until the fish become acclimatized, which should take 5 or 6 weeks. Usually this will apply only to fish that have just come in from the wild; many *Corydoras* that we buy are commercially bred and are therefore used to many different water conditions.

Responsible dealers will always give you information on the water conditions in which their stock is kept and they will usually do all they can to help you achieve the right conditions for your fish.

If you need to make changes in your water conditions, please do so carefully and slowly, so as not to distress the fish. If you wish to adjust the chemical balance of the water, ask your dealer which test-kits to use and how best to soften the water etc.

Maintenance of Water Quality

Water, in the natural environment, is subject to change because of the effects of rain or wind. The presence of living animals and plants in the aquarium produces waste-products from several sources. Fish excrete liquid and solid matter, which in turn produce ammonia. Leaves of plants die and decompose, uneaten food will rot, the water often discolours and sometimes begins to smell, and, without actually re-creating a flowing stream in the aquarium, we can attempt to purify the water by partial water-changes and filtration.

Filtration

The equipment used for filtration is mainly mechanical, chemical or
biological.

Box-filters   These pass dirty aquarium water through different mediums
and then return the cleaned water to the aquarium. The dirty water is
passed first through a medium, which traps the suspended material, and
then through a layer of activated carbon which removes dissolved waste
products; finally it is passed through a nylon floss to take out anything
that is left. (Glass wool should *not* be used as a medium because tiny
fragments could pass into the aquarium and possibly injure your fish.)
These types of filters are internal or external and can be driven by an
electric motor or an air-pump.

Filters containing activated carbon should always be turned off when
medication is being used in the aquarium because the carbon will absorb
the medication. In this instance it is best to use an air-stone in the tank
until the medication has done its job.

In addition to a box-filter, many aquarists use air-stones or corner-
filters that are run by pumps – either piston or vibrator types. Piston-
pumps can be more expensive, and require more regular maintenance,
but they are quieter than some of the cheaper vibrator-pumps.

The vibrator-pump is the most popular and is available in many sizes.
The air is pumped through plastic tubing into an air-stone (that can be
housed inside your corner-filter). From the air-stone, a cascade of
bubbles will rise to the top of your aquarium. This, of course, will
introduce more oxygen into the water.

Biological filters   These are nature's own way of dealing with waste-
products. The filter makes use of the aquarium's gravel as a filter-bed
and the gravel should be at least 5 cm deep. The water passes through
the gravel and bacteria develop throughout the entire gravel bed. This
filter is usually operated by an air-pump, although, if an extra flow is
needed, a non-submersible electric pump can be mounted on top of the
biological filter's lift-tube. An under-gravel filter should never be
switched off. If it is, as soon as the water flow stops, the bacteria will
begin to die off and the filter action will be lost.

In case of power failure, it is always advisable to invest in a battery-
operated air-pump. Usually, during a power failure, the temperature
goes down only very slowly, but the lack of oxygen will affect the fish
very quickly. Battery-pumps are also a good thing to have if you need to
move fish at any time.

Water-changes

Carry out a partial water-change every week, even if you are using an external filter. It does not have to be a large amount – 10 l or so will do, and this will help to keep your fish healthy. It is best not to use water directly from the tap. The fresh water should always be allowed to stand for at least 48 hours. It is advisable to keep a plastic dustbin or barrel filled with fresh water on hand at all times because you never know when it might be needed. Of course, if you have a fish-house, it is a good idea to keep 1 large tank filled with fresh water. It will always come in handy for an emergency.

Many people use water directly from the tap and add dechlorinators etc., but if you can avoid doing this it is all the better for your fish.

Heating

The type of heating you use depends on how many tanks you are keeping. If you only have one or two, the best type is the combined heater/thermostat. Today's modern equipment is very good, simple to install and safe to handle. The heaters are thermostatically controlled and therefore electricity consumption is not too high. The majority of aquarists use these combined units. They need minimal wiring and have largely taken over from the separate heater and thermostat that have been used by fish-keepers for many years.

With a large tank it is best to use 2 units – one at either end. This gives a more even temperature in the tank and, in the event of one failing, you always have the other there as a back-up.

If you have a fish-house or fish-room, it is more economical to heat the room than the individual tanks. Many aquarists who custom-build their fish-houses run their own central-heating system and can adjust the temperatures as necessary. This, of course, can be most advantageous when one is trying to breed different species.

Alternatively, heating pads can be used. The aquarium rests on the pad and so there are no heaters or thermostats to clutter the tank.

The latest item on the market is the heater-cable. These are now available in 4 capacities – 15W, 25W, 50W and 100W – and can be purchased at a reasonable price from many aquatic shops. The cable should be laid in a snake-like pattern on the base of the aquarium (fixing-suckers are included with the cable). The substrate then covers the cable and the heat rises evenly through the substrate, all round the tank. A cable is often used in conjunction with different substrates to help promote a healthy plant growth.

A thermometer of some sort should always be placed somewhere in (or on) the tank and glanced at every day to confirm that the heaters are working.

Many aquarists keep their fish at too high a temperature. Most of the aquariums one encounters are kept at temperatures of 25–27°C, but many fish seem happier when kept at a more natural temperature of 21–24°C.

In the event of a power failure, the temperature will usually fall quite slowly, especially in a large tank. This is not really a cause for concern unless the power is going to be off for a long period of time. As soon as the power goes off, cover the tank with a blanket (or something similar) to conserve the heat. If the power is off for a long time, bottles or bags of heated water may be floated in the tank to keep up the temperature. This is a situation in which a battery-powered air-pump becomes invaluable because, as mentioned previously, lack of oxygen is usually the first thing to affect the fish.

Lighting

Aquarium plants need light to photosynthesise. In their natural habitat, the sun shines down on the water and provides an essential stimulus to the fish and plants.

Lights can easily be incorporated into the aquarium by means of bulbs or tubes mounted in the aquarium hood. Tungsten lamps are easy to install, and cheap to buy, but they get very hot and burn a fair amount of electricity. (I would not recommend this type of lighting as it is quite dangerous and, by the time this book is published, it may no longer be legal.) Fluorescent tubes are more expensive to buy but quite cheap to run. They do not get as hot as bulbs and produce an even light across the aquarium.

Most hoods today come with either ready-made holes for tungsten lamp-fittings or clips for fluorescent tubes. In some hoods, there is even space for the starter-equipment to be housed.

To simulate the fish's natural light is more or less impossible, but fluorescent tubes seem to function very well in the home aquarium. Plants require different amounts of light for optimum growth and there are several fluorescent tubes on the market just to help plant growth. Some aquarists in this country combine 2 or 3 different colour spectra in order to obtain the correct intensity for their plants and fish. Dutch aquarists seem to practise 'underwater gardening'. Their tanks are very heavily planted and really look like a moving picture. Naturally, they need a very high intensity of light, and many of their tanks are lit by between 6 and 10 fluorescent tubes, each coming on and going off in a different sequence.

Lighting is not so important in breeding-tanks. *Corydoras* seem to be unaffected by whatever type of lighting is used, but, of course, lights are necessary if their aquarium is planted.

It is advisable to have a cover-glass on the aquarium. This will reduce water loss by evaporation and prevent water being splashed on to the lights and equipment housed in the hood. It will also prevent the fish from jumping out of the aquarium and your floating plants (if you have any) from scorching. The cover-glass should be kept clean in order to minimize light loss.

Plants in the Aquarium

The choice of plants is always a matter of individual taste. There are many different forms and colours available and they not only help to maintain a well-balanced and healthy aquarium but also provide shade, spawning-sites and occasional refuge for the fish.

Plants should be selected to occupy different areas of the aquarium – from floor-covering miniature plants to floating plants covering the water's surface. Leaf form will vary from broad to feathery and colours will range from light green to dark green, some leaves even having a purplish or red underside.

Not all aquarium plants root in the substrate. Some species cling to the surface of submerged logs or rocks whilst others float freely on the surface of the water, their hair-like roots trailing beneath and providing refuge for tiny fishes.

When planting out a tank for small fish, including *Corydoras*, make sure you leave the front (where you usually feed the fish) clear. *Corydoras* will sift the substrate for food and you don't want any plants disturbed by this activity.

Generally, tall plants (*Vallisneria*, *Sagittaria*, *Ambulia* or *Cabomba*) should be placed at the back and sides of the tank. Some of the smaller *Cryptocoryne* and dwarf grasses are best in the foreground. Specimen plants, such as *Echinodoras*, *Aponogeton* and *Cryptocoryne willisii*, are very suitable for the middle area of the tank. These are just a few of the many aquarium plants available from good stockists, who will be only too pleased to advise you on planting-out your tank.

Some *Corydoras* will spawn on the broader-leaved plants, so plant the tank accordingly. Many plants can now be purchased in their own little pots which can be put straight into the substrate.

Before introducing the plants into the aquarium, rinse them thoroughly in a mild aquarium-disinfectant, e.g. dilute potassium permanganate solution, and check them for snails, eggs or any other unwanted items. If snails are introduced into the aquarium, it is very difficult to get rid of them.

Lay-out

The layout of the aquarium depends on whether it is to be a community aquarium in the living-room, or a breeding-tank in the fish-room or fish-house.

A community aquarium that is to be the focal point in a room in your home will need to look like a 'living' or 'moving' picture. You will have to decide whether you are going to furnish the tank with rocks, slate or wood, or with a mixture of all 3.

The gravel should not be too coarse (uneaten food can get trapped in it) or too fine (it can impede the flow of water in a biological filter and stop the root-growth of some plants).

Ideally, if you intend to keep *Corydoras*, a small 'pea' gravel should be used. *Corydoras* burrow into the gravel looking for food and, if the gravel is too large or too sharp, it can damage their barbels which play an essential role in breeding (see p. 37). Rock caves provide ideal hiding-places for some of the more timid fish and, using rocks or slate, it is possible to build a variety of hiding-places. Use silicone adhesive to keep them in place and thus prevent any 'rock falls'.

Tree roots are another ideal item for furnishing the aquarium. In the wild, the fish shoal around roots of submerged trees, so the aquarium can be made to look like part of a river or stream. Before introducing tree roots into your aquarium, check first with your local shop because not all wood is safe to use in the aquarium.

Synthetic decorations are often used as they are readily available in the shops and do not stain the water in the aquarium. These days, they are very realistic and a piece of synthetic wood looks very effective with some Java Moss clinging to it.

Breeding-tanks are normally managed in a completely different way, depending on the species which is being bred and the mediums which are being used to encourage spawning.

Decorating the aquarium is often a compromise between the needs of the fish and what the aquarist thinks will look natural. If the fish are content in their surroundings, then you should be pleased with the finished results.

5

Stocking the Aquarium

In order to obtain good specimens, great care should be taken over the selection and purchase of fish. A period of quarantine is also advisable in order to prevent the introduction of disease into established aquariums.

Purchasing Stock

When selecting *Corydoras*, the first consideration is their health. Look for signs of disease and damage. If the fish have been kept in good conditions they will be alert and have fairly good colour; damaged or split fins are not too much of a problem as these will quickly heal, but make sure that there are no obvious fungal or bacterial infections. Avoid buying fish that behave in an unusual manner (e.g. dashing nervously around the tank or brushing against the rocks or substrate). Check that they have both eyes (this is quite a common failing) and check their barbels. If the barbels are very badly worn, don't buy them as they don't always grow back.

Many shop-keepers automatically label their fish with the names under which they were imported – and these names are not always correct. If the shop-owner is unable to identify a particular species of fish, the 'imported' name is the only one he can give, so you must make sure that the fish you are buying is the species which you are looking for. In the past, I have travelled miles to some particular shop which had advertised a fish that I was looking for – only to get there and find that it had been misidentified and was a completely different species.

Selecting breeding-stock from newly-imported fish can sometimes be a problem. When fish are first imported, they are often very thin, possibly because of a long spell in the holding-tanks before being exported. For this reason, body shape is not always a good guide when sexing fish. There are, of course, some species that are almost impossible to sex, even when both sexes are present, and others that can be sexed by their colour pattern (see Chapter 9). If the fish have arrived in fairly good condition, it is often easy to recognize a female by the plumper body shape (see p. 35) If this is not apparent, then look at the shape of the ventral fins (see p. 36) because, in most species, the male has longer and more pointed ventral fins than the female.

If you can afford them, it is best to purchase 4 or 6 specimens. *Corydoras* are shoaling fish and, if you have bought a number of specimens, you are more likely to get at least 1 pair. If you can wait for your fish to grow, it is always best to buy several young specimens rather than 1 or 2 adults. Younger fish are usually a little cheaper and will be with you for longer.

Transporting Fish

The majority of South American catfish on sale have been directly imported and, like any wild-caught animal, they must be given time to adjust to their new environment.

Some shippers pack their fish very well: not too many to a bag, plenty of air, just enough water. I was once at an importer's premises when fish were brought in from the airport and, when the boxes were opened, the smell knocked me back. The exporters had packed too many fish in the bag, the bag had possibly become deflated, the water looked frothy and it was extremely unlikely that any fish from the shipment could be saved.

Those are the two extremes. In general most fish are packed well these days, although some fish still arrive in very poor condition. In many cases this is due to the health of the fish at the time of packing. Many holding-tanks are overcrowded, the water is not always as clean as it could be, and the fish, as a result, are more likely to be diseased. Once the fish are 'bagged', diseases are easily spread and many of the fish arrive dead or very stressed. Those that survive a bad shipment are often very weak and prone to more diseases. Most importers will quarantine these fish, but occasionally a few slip through.

Fish purchased from good aquatic shops are normally packed well. It is advisable, when going out specifically to buy fish, to make sure that you are equipped to do so. If you are going by car, always take an old blanket in the boot and either a cardboard or polystyrene box. Your purchases can then be placed in the box and the blanket can be wrapped around it. Of course, if you are using public transport this is impossible, but you can take a fairly large bag and some old newspapers for insulation.

The usual method of transporting a fish is in a clear plastic bag. Avoiding shock is probably the most important thing when moving fish, so, once you get the fish home, and before you float the bag in the tank, turn out the aquarium light; a darkened tank will help the fish to settle down. Float the bag containing the fish in the tank until the water in the bag reaches the same temperature as the water in the tank. Before releasing the fish, mix some of your aquarium water with the water in the bag so that the fish can become accustomed to the new water. If your water is very different from that of your supplier this procedure should be carried out very slowly, and may take a couple of hours. If the fish shows no sign of distress, release it into the tank. At first, the fish will probably try to find somewhere to hide; this is quite natural, so allow it time to settle in before giving it a little food. It can sometimes be difficult to get a wild-caught fish to accept food in an aquarium, so be patient.

Introducing New Fish to the Aquarium

All new fish that are purchased should be quarantined. We have all taken chances and put new fish straight into the breeding- or community tank and, on many occasions, have got away with it. Nevertheless, there is always the one occasion when you can wipe out a whole tank of fish by adding just one specimen which subsequently transfers a disease because it has not been quarantined.

The fish you have just purchased may look extremely healthy (and possibly is), but you really don't know. Set up a tank (see p. 32) especially for quarantining your fish. It does not need to be very big; 46 cm × 25 cm × 25 cm will do.

After equalizing the water temperatures, release your newly-purchased fish from its bag into the quarantine tank. Do not add any medication if the fish is looking well; just leave it in the tank for 10–14 days. If after this time the fish has not developed any disease, it can be transferred to the community or breeding-tank.

If any disease becomes apparent, treat the fish with a suitable medication, according to the instructions on the container. Leave the fish in the quarantine tank for at least 10 days after the disease has cleared up.

Some newly-purchased fish look healthy but can be stressed from having just been imported. Quarantining helps them recover and acclimatize to their new conditions.

6
Diet

A varied diet is as necessary for fish as it is for us. Such a diet will ensure that they receive all the proteins, vitamins and other requirements necessary for their well-being.

After years of research and development, fish in captivity are possibly better fed than their counterparts in the wild. The quantity and quality of food is down to us – their owners.

Some fish take their food from the surface of the water, some as the food is falling through the water, and others from the aquarium floor. It is therefore necessary to cater for all these fish.

Types of Fish-foods

Dried Foods

The majority of foods that we feed to fish are manufactured and are mostly in flake, granular or tablet form. Most of the flake floats on the surface to begin with, then gradually sinks to the bottom of the aquarium, thus meeting the needs of all types of fish.

Fish should not be over-fed, i.e. too much food should never be put into the tank at one time. The fish themselves will not over-feed – they will eat only what they need and leave the rest on the substrate – but, if the food is left uneaten on the bottom of the aquarium, it will decompose and pollute the water. More fish have been killed in this way than in any other. Feed the fish 2 or 3 times a day, giving them a small amount of food each time (as much as they can eat in 2 or 3 minutes). Make sure that a last feed is given at night (of a food that sinks) so that the nocturnal bottom-dwellers are fed.

Normal flake-food (whichever brand you prefer) can be fed to all your fish. Many manufacturers also produce foods for herbivores and carnivores, and also a special food for baby fish. Colour-enhancing foods are also manufactured. These contain carotene which is supposed to enhance the red colour in the fish.

Tablet foods and granules sink to the bottom of the aquarium. The tablets slowly dissolve and so get eaten by most fish. The larger types of granules are usually enjoyed by cichlids and larger catfish.

It is possible to feed fish on a staple diet of dried food, but it is best to give them supplementary foods, especially when you are trying to get fish into optimum condition for breeding.

Freeze-dried Foods

There are many freeze-dried foods available: *Tubifex* worms, *Mysis* shrimps etc. *Tubifex* cubes are easily stuck to the aquarium glass and will be eaten by all the fish. They are a very good supplement to flake-food.

Frozen Foods

There are many frozen foods on the market now, sold in 'blister packs' which contain feed-sized blocks. The packaging is transparent so that you can see what you are buying. Some of the foods available are: Mosquito larvae, *Cyclops*, *Daphnia* (Water Fleas), red plankton, *Artemia* (Brine Shrimps), *Mysis* shrimps, krill, mussel, roe, cockle, shrimps, *Tubifex*, a special *Discus* food and a cichlid food. There are also many 'flat-pack' frozen foods for sale, including all those named above and more. Thus, there is plenty to tempt all types of fish.

There is also a food that can be prepared and frozen at home. Get some beef heart from a local butcher, cut off all the fat and mince it very finely. Add to this some freshly-cooked spinach (frozen will also do, but *not* tinned). Place a small amount of the mixture in a plastic bag, flatten it out and freeze it. A number of bags can be prepared in this way. They are easy to store and do not take up much room in the freezer. When required, just break off a piece of the mixture, let it thaw and drop it into the aquarium. This should only be fed once or twice a week, and only in small amounts. Always make sure that any uneaten surplus is siphoned off. Alternatively, instead of freezing it flat, pack the minced food into ice-cube trays and freeze it. You can then pop out a cube whenever it is needed. Many aquarists have their own secret recipes, with all sorts of ingredients.

Live Foods

Many experienced aquarists enhance the diet of their fish with Earthworms (a very good source of protein), *Tubifex*, shrimps, *Daphnia*, Bloodworms, Whiteworms, Microworms and Brine Shrimps.

Whiteworms (*Enchytraeus albidus*) and Microworms (*Anguillila silusiae*) Cultures are readily available from good shops and are sold with instructions telling you how to keep and feed the cultures. Microworms are a very good food for young fish.

Brine Shrimps (*Artemia* sp.)   These shrimps are purchased as eggs which need to be hatched in salt water. All the details on hatching them out appear on the packaging (see also Foods for Baby Fish, opposite). Newly-hatched Brine Shrimps are an excellent food for young fish.

Water Fleas (*Daphnia*)   These small crustaceans do not live very long once they have been caught, so they need to be fed to the fish fairly quickly. There may be a pond nearby where they are breeding, so take a net with you next time you go for a walk and see if you can catch some. They are an excellent food.

Bloodworms   These are readily taken by most fish and are sold in many aquatic shops. They make a very good food, but should only be fed to the fish once or twice a week. The worms should be blood-red in colour – if they look doubtful, don't use them.

Tubifex   This live food was used constantly by aquarists many years ago and caused no problems. When living in London, I used to purchase my *Tubifex* from a man who had one of the very few licences that were issued for collecting it. It was gathered at low tide from the mud in the River Thames. The Thames has now been cleaned up a great deal and there are no longer any *Tubifex* there. It is still sold, however, but I believe that it now comes from somewhere in the north of England. To keep it fresh, put it into a container with water continually running over it. It is now claimed by many people to be the cause of disease, so it is not used so frequently these days.

Earthworms   Large fish will take this excellent live food whole, but you may have to chop up the worms for the smaller species. Your own garden is probably an ideal source but remember never to collect them from an area where chemicals of any sort have been used. If you are quick enough, you can catch Earthworms when they come up on the lawn on a warm moist evening. If not, you will just have to turn over the compost and collect them from there. Some shops sell them – mostly for freshwater fishermen. If chopped really small, Earthworms are a very good food for small fish. They are a good source of protein and are often used as a supplementary food to bring *Corydoras* into breeding condition.

Other Foods

Not all fish will take to these foods right away. You may need to try some a few times before you get any results.

Prawns and Cooked Chicken   These are both good foods when fed in small quantities. Most fish will eat them and, if chopped very small, they are excellent for young fish.

Peas It is best to use frozen peas. Let them thaw out, place them in boiling water for a few minutes and then drain. You can then 'pop' them out of their skins and drop them into the tank.

Spinach Never use tinned spinach which contains too many additives that are not good for the fish. Frozen spinach is fine, but fresh is even better. Put it into boiling water for a few minutes, chop it up, let it cool and then feed it to the fish. Feed only in small quantities.

Lettuce Crush a couple of lettuce leaves in the hand, weight them down and drop them into the aquarium. You will be surprised at the different species that will graze on them.

Potato Peel a potato, immerse it in boiling water for about 5 minutes, allow it to cool and then drop it into the aquarium. When the potato begins to go black, remove it from the tank.

Foods for Baby Fish

Nowadays, baby fish can be well catered for with both manufactured and live foods. One of the best live foods is newly-hatched Brine Shrimps. Eggs can be purchased and stored for a long time in an air-tight container; to hatch them, add the dry eggs to a solution of salt water and agitate the solution with an air-stone until hatching occurs. The live shrimps should then be strained through a net and rinsed in fresh water before feeding.

Manufactured fry-foods come in liquid and powder forms, for either egg-laying or livebearing fish.

Baby fish should not be fed until they are free-swimming and the yolk sac has been absorbed.

7
Diseases

Aquarists can do a great deal to ensure that their fish do not contract diseases. Start by making sure that any stock you buy looks healthy and free from any obvious disease. Even healthy-looking fish that have just been purchased should be quarantined before putting them into your community or breeding-tanks.

Plants can also introduce diseases and pests. Any plant should be rinsed in a weak solution of either potassium permanganate (available from a chemist) or a proprietary brand of aquarium disinfectant. This should destroy any unwanted aquatic life on the plant leaves.

Aquarium nets can also spread disease from tank to tank. If you cannot keep a net to each tank, then make sure that it is washed in either disinfectant or boiling water before it is used again.

Avoid using anything near the aquarium that gives off strong fumes (paint, spray polish, air-freshener sprays), because they can be transferred to the aquarium via the air-pump.

Keep your tanks clean. Dirty water can also bring on diseases.

Apart from quarantining the fish, you should always keep a separate tank as a hospital tank. All you need is:

- A tank with no gravel on its base.
- A corner-filter, filled with nylon wool (one with an air-stone attachment is ideal to keep the water aerated).
- A couple of plastic plants to give the fish a feeling of security. Don't use live plants because some medications can harm them.
- A heater and external thermostat for easier temperature control.
- One or two flower-pots for the fish to hide in.

It is easier to introduce medication into a fairly bare tank – with no plants or filter mediums. You then have only the fish to worry about.

Mentioned below are a few of the common diseases found in fish.

Red-blotch Disease

This often occurs in newly-imported *Corydoras*. It has been discussed at length over the years by both aquarists and ichthyologists, but no satisfactory cause has ever been proved. It has been suggested that the use of pure oxygen in the bags in which the fish are transported from the wild causes damage to the gut of any *Corydoras* that has been up to the surface of the water for air. Other people have thought that the many different water-changes to which the *Corydoras* are subjected from capture to aquarium set up some bacterial activity in the gut but this, too, has never been proved. Some fish die very quickly, others recover, but there is no definite cure known.

Anchor Worms

These little worms can usually be seen sticking out from under the scutes. They can carefully be removed with a pair of tweezers, and the area can then be bathed with a mild aquarium-disinfectant.

Whitespot (*Ichthyophthirius multifiliis*)

This is a very common parasitic ailment. Tiny white spots cover the body and fins of the fish. This disease is of a cyclic nature. The parasite falls from the body of an infected fish on to the floor of the aquarium where it forms a cyst; from this emerge hundreds of young parasites which become free-swimming and start to look for a new host. This disease, once established in 1 fish, will usually spread to all the others, so it is best to treat the whole tank. Many aquarists think that this disease lies dormant in every aquarium, ready to infect weakened fish. There are a number of remedies available, but the instructions should be read carefully and overdosing avoided at all costs. For catfish, I would recommend the use of only half the recommended dose. This low level of medication may cure the fish less quickly, but it is also less likely to harm them. Whitespot has been known to be more difficult to cure in armoured fish (callichthyids, doradids and loricariids).

Dropsy

With this disease, the scales of the fish protrude noticeably (rather like those of a pearl-scaled goldfish), due to accumulated liquid in the body. Remove the infected fish as soon as you see it. Fish have been known to recover from this ailment but, at the time of going to press, there is no known cure.

Ulcers

Ulcers are caused by bacterial infection and are most often seen on newly-imported fish with a low resistance to infection (possibly resulting from bad handling during importation). The first signs are reddening at the base of the fins and on parts of the body. If caught at an early stage, ulcers can be treated with the usual bactericides but, if allowed to take hold, it is more difficult to treat and can then spread to the healthy inhabitants of the aquarium. If this happens, you will probably have to treat the whole tank with antibiotics (which can be obtained from your local veterinary surgeon).

Rot

Tailrot and finrot often appear on fish that are in poor health. They are often caused by unhygienic conditions in the tank which encourage bacterial growth. Proprietary cures will assist recovery.

Intestinal Worms

Usually, these worms are not visible externally. When a fish is heavily infested, however, the worms may be seen protruding from the vent. This little worm is normally introduced into the aquarium by newly-imported fish, but can also be introduced by infected live food. The infection can spread throughout the tank. There are drugs available to cure this worm, but they can only be obtained from a veterinary surgeon. Any dead fish should be removed immediately in case other inhabitants of the tank should decide to eat them and thereby become infected.

Eye Infections

These are often caused by the fish knocking their eyes on rocks or other objects in the tank, making the eye cloud over. This can often be cured by bathing the eye with a mild aquarium-disinfectant. Aquarists have been known to use a brand of eye-wash that is normally used for human beings.

'Pop-eye'

The cause of this is uncertain. It can result from an eye infection that has not responded to treatment, but usually indicates the presence of some other disease. It sometimes just goes away, but there is no known cure.

Skin Fluke

This parasite burrows into the surface of the fish's skin. It responds well to proprietary treatments which are readily available.

Fish often show warning signs that all is not well in the tank. Check your fish every day because, in most cases, a water-change is usually all that is required to rectify the situation. If your tank is regularly maintained, most diseases can be kept at bay.

8
Breeding

With over 120 species of *Corydoras*, you can well imagine the varied range of conditions necessary for successful breeding. What suits one species will not necessarily suit another, so it is advisable to simulate as broad a range of conditions as possible. Before breeding attempts can be made, you must be sure that both sexes are present and that the fish are in good health and optimum condition.

Sexing Fish

It is not always easy to determine the sex of *Corydoras*. Indeed, when some shipments arrive, it is more or less impossible due to the poor state of the fish. In this instance, it is best to buy about 6 specimens and feed them up. When they are in good health, you will probably be able to sex them. Body shape is not always the best guide, although when your fish are in good condition, you can usually recognize the plumper body shape of the female (Fig. 2).

If the sexual differences are not obvious from the body shape alone, then you must look at the shape of the fins. In most species, the male has longer, more pointed, ventral fins (Fig. 3), and quite often the pectoral and dorsal fin spines are slightly longer.

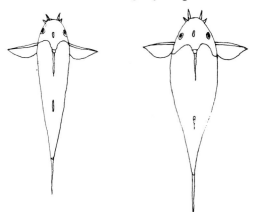

Fig. 2 Sexual differences in *Corydoras*. Body shape: male (left), female (right).

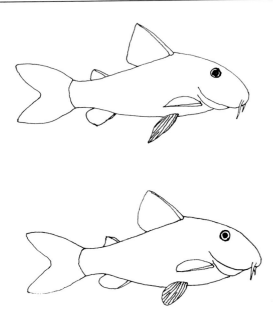

Fig. 3 Sexual differences in *Corydoras*. Fin shape: male (top), female (bottom).

In *C. barbatus* (Quoy & Gaimard, 1824), the head of the male is margined with bristles in the front of the pre-operculum, but this is only obvious in an adult fish. The male also has a prolonged pectoral fin spine and extended first and second soft dorsal fin rays.

Breeding Biology

For breeding purposes, the water is best kept at about 21°C. The size of the breeding-tank is not particularly important, although most *Corydoras* breeders that I know prefer to use a 46 cm × 25 cm × 25 cm tank. The size of the substrate (see p. 24) *is* important in preventing damage to the barbels. The barbels have a special purpose in the mating sequence and if they are too badly worn the fish become almost impossible to breed.

Feeding Breeding-stock

Food is a very important factor in getting fish into breeding condition. They should be fed a wide variety of foods, especially live foods. Small amounts, given a few times each day, will bring fish into breeding condition very quickly.

Spawning

For the spawning-attempt, it is advisable to use 2 males to every female. The basic spawning-pattern will be described first, and then some of the variations.

The first indication of a spawning being imminent is the males starting to chase the female around the tank and performing little dances in front of them. As the female becomes more interested, she may be seen cleaning various spots around the aquarium. (This cleaning activity only occurs with species that prefer to lay their eggs on solid objects.) After a period of time (which can be minutes or hours), the male will start to offer himself, arched sideways on, in front of a favourite female. Provided that she is ready, she will nuzzle into his ventral area and he will then grip her barbels with his pectoral fin spines. (This is why the barbels must be kept in good condition.) Once the male and female are locked in this formation, known as the 'T' position, both fish will start quivering, the female continuing to push into the side of the male. At this point, the male will release his milt and the female will release several eggs into her ventral fins, which she forms into a pouch.

The actual method of fertilization is still something of a mystery; the main theory is that the female takes the milt into her mouth, then passes it out through her gills and along the underside of her body, using pectoral fin movements to direct the flow to her ventral fin pouch.

There are, however, many variations of this behaviour. In *C. barbatus*, the female does most of the chasing; she will drive into the side of the male, sending him from one side of the tank to the other, and then, when she has gathered his milt, she will break free, settle on the bottom, lean over on 1 pectoral fin spine and then, while making a paddling motion with her other pectoral fin, release several eggs into her ventral fin pouch. She then deposits her eggs all together in a tight cluster, usually near the surface. This whole procedure usually takes no more than an hour from start to finish. *C. metae* Eigenmann, 1914, which spawns in a similar manner, will take several hours, although the eggs will be spread all over the place.

One species uses a completely different method of mating and that is *C. elegans* Steindachner, 1877. Instead of assuming the conventional 'T' position, the fish face each other and quiver; the female then deposits several eggs into her ventral fin pouch and swims off, hotly pursued by the male. Once the female has positioned her eggs, the male follows behind and passes closely over them (in cichlid fashion), as though making sure that they are all fertilized. The percentage of infertile eggs is usually very low.

Once you are satisfied that the spawning sequence has finished, remove the adult fish. Some species will eat their eggs or the newly-hatched fry. In some cases, a few drops of methylene blue should be added to the tank, to prevent the development of fungus on any unfertilized eggs and the contamination of the healthy ones.

In the wild, *Corydoras* usually spawn during the rainy season. The cooler rain-water entering the river system often stimulates the fish and this can be emulated in your breeding-tank by the addition of some cold water. As the rivers begin to flood, more spawning-sites become available to the fish and many different foods are swept into the water.

The size of *Corydoras* eggs varies and is not necessarily related to the size of the species. Large species, such as *C. zygatus* Eigenmann & Allen, 1942, *C. treitlii* Steindachner, 1902, and *C. amapaensis* Nijssen, 1972, lay eggs no bigger than 1.5 mm in diameter, whereas the smaller *C. metae*, *C. garbei* R. Von Ihering, 1911, and *C. pygmaeus* Knaack, 1966, all lay large eggs of over 2 mm in diameter; *C. garbei* eggs are the largest recorded and measure 2.5 mm in diameter. As a general rule, however, the species which lay small eggs do so in large numbers; a *C. zygatus* female can lay up to 400 eggs at a spawning, whereas *C. garbei* usually lays no more than 20.

Depending on the water temperature, it usually takes 3–4 days for the eggs to hatch. They will take longer if the temperature is below 21°C. Once the eggs have hatched, it will take a further 2 days for the fry to absorb the yolk sac, after which time very small foods should be given, such as Microworms, newly-hatched Brine Shrimps and powdered flake (pre-soaked so that it sinks right away).

As the fry grow, they can be fed on slightly larger foods and, where there are a large number of fry, they should be separated into several tanks to obtain the best possible growth rate. This is fairly rapid in most species, but, of course, there are exceptions: *C. pygmaeus* can reach adulthood and be sexually mature in 3 months – but some other species take up to 9 months to reach maturity.

For new species, or species that, as far as you know, have not been bred, furnish a tank with different types of spawning-mediums. Try nylon mops suspended from a cork, a few broad-leaved plants, pieces of wood, or even Java Moss spread across the bottom of the tank. Some species like to spawn on the tank sides only; others have a particular preference in regard to their spawning-site, so cover every possible variation. It is not advisable to use under-gravel filters in the breeding-tank. The filter action will draw the newly-hatched fry down into the gravel and a large percentage will be lost. Box-filters are best as they are easy to remove and clean.

In Chapter 9, you will find breeding-details as well as line drawings of many *Corydoras* species showing different stages in their development. As you will see, the juveniles look nothing like the adult fish.

9
Corydoras Catfish Species

Corydoras acrensis
Nijssen, 1972

Taxonomic Details
First collected in 1967 by J. P. Gosse, *C. acrensis* is known from a single specimen.

ETYMOLOGY Named after Acre, the location where the fish was collected.

Distribution
Brazil: Acre – Furo de Lago Sāo, Francisco, a tributary at the left bank of Rio Jurua.

Description
SIZE The largest specimen examined was 30 mm, but this fish should grow to 55 mm in the aquarium.

Corydoras acutus
Cope, 1872
Black-top Corydoras

Taxonomic Details
ETYMOLOGY From the Latin *acutus* = 'sharp', alluding to the shape of the snout. The common name is derived from the large black blotch on the dorsal fin.

Distribution
Ecuador: Pastaza – Jatun Cocha at Rio Yasuni, Rio Napo system. Peru: Loreto – Rio Ampiyacu, Rio Yavari and Rio Huytoyacu.

Description
C. acutus is sometimes confused with *C. stenocephalus*, whose body proportions are the same, but which displays a completely different colour pattern. In some specimens of *C. acutus* the pigment on the body is more dense and forms irregular lines whereas *C. stenocephalus* has 1 or 2 large blotches on the body. The dark pigment on the junction of the body scutes sometimes forms a zigzag line and the blotch in the dorsal fin (which is absent in *C. stenocephalus*) varies in size and colour from jet black to brown. The caudal fin can have 4–11 irregular vertical bars (these are absent in *C. stenocephalus*).

SIZE The largest specimen examined was 55 mm but this fish should grow to 70 mm in the aquarium.

Breeding
SPAWNING This species spawns in the typical 'T' formation. It usually lays its eggs in Java Moss and in the corners of the tank. The eggs are approximately 1.5 mm in diameter and hatch in 4 days.

FEEDING The fry should be first fed 3 days after hatching and small amounts

Black-top Corydoras (*Corydoras acutus*). Adult. Note the black blotch on the dorsal fin from which it gets its common name.

of Microworms and soaked, powdered flake should be given. After another 3 days, newly-hatched Brine Shrimps can be introduced and these should be fed every other day. As the fry grow, the size and variety of the foods should be increased (chopped *Tubifex*, sifted *Daphnia* and Grindal Worms).

FRY   Adult coloration is reached in 8–10 weeks.

Corydoras adolfoi
Burgess, 1982
Adolfo's Corydoras

Taxonomic Details
First collected by Dr H. Axelrod in 1982.

ETYMOLOGY Named in honour of Adolfo Schwartz.

Distribution
Brazil: Upper Rio Negro.

Description
SIZE   The largest specimen examined was 57.7 mm but this species should grow to 60 mm in the aquarium.

Breeding
This species has been bred under aquarium conditions.

Corydoras aeneus
(Gill, 1858)
Bronze Catfish

Taxonomic Details
ETYMOLOGY   From the Latin *aeneus* = 'copper' or 'bronze'.

SYNONYMS
Hoplosoma aeneum Gill, 1858
C. microps Eigenmann & Kennedy, 1903
C. venezuelanus R. Von Ihering, 1911
C. macrosteus Regan, 1912
C. schultzei Holly, 1940

Distribution

Trinidad: In clear streams on the island. Peru: Ucayali – Rio Ucayali system, a tributary of Rio Pachitea, Rio Chivis and Rio Pichis. Ecuador: Napo – Rio Napo system and Rio Jivino. Colombia: Orinoco River system. Venezuela: Carobobo – Rio Cabriales, Valencia. Brazil: Mato Grosso – a small lagoon near Rio Branco, Arcgua, a brook into Laguna Ypacara; São Paulo – Rio Piracicaba.

Description

C. aeneus is one of the commonest and most readily available species of *Corydoras*. It is also one of the most widely-distributed species in tropical South America. There are several different colour variations (see p. 42), not including the popular Albino strain. These colour variations have been the basis of a number of new names that are now known to be synonyms.

C. aeneus is one of the species where the female grows larger than the male. It is bred commercially in Singapore and is an ideal fish for the beginner to keep, being fairly easy to breed. Gill (who described this species) wrote in his field notes that 'this fish is very abundant in the clear streams of the island of Trinidad, and lives in numbers of twenty or thirty, or even more. It attains a length from two and a half to three and sometimes even four inches'. Nijssen and Isbrücker state 'with regard to the maximum size recorded by Gill, no specimens with a total length of 100 mm (four inches) are known. Therefore we assume it to be an exaggerated estimation in the field'. It is nice to know that even in 1858 fishermen were exaggerating the size of the fish they had caught!

SIZE The largest specimen examined was 56.2 mm but, in the aquarium, males should grow to 65 mm and females to 75 mm. The Albino strain should grow to 65 mm (males) and 70 mm (females).

Bronze Catfish (*Corydoras aeneus*). Adult. A fully-grown female is larger than the male. This species is easy to breed and ideal for the novice aquarist.

Corydoras aeneus. Regional colour variations.

Breeding

SPAWNING   This usually follows a cold-water-change that has reduced the temperature from 21°C to 16°C. The fish breed in typical 'T' formation. The eggs are approximately 1.5 mm in diameter and are laid in clusters around the tank. The eggs take 3–4 days to hatch. The Albino strain lays smaller eggs (1 mm diameter), but in larger numbers: as many as 400 in a single spawning.

FEEDING   As for *C. acutus* (p. 39).

FRY   Adult coloration is reached in 9–10 weeks.

Corydoras agassizii
Steindachner, 1877
Agassiz's Corydoras

Taxonomic Details
First collected in 1865 by the Thayer Expedition.

ETYMOLOGY   Named in honour of Professor Louis Agassiz, a famous Swiss zoologist who emigrated to the USA and founded the Museum of Comparative Zoology at Harvard.

Distribution
Brazil: Amazonas – Rio Amazonas near Tabatinga. Peru: Huanuco – Rio Pachitea; Loreto – Rio Nanay and Rio Napo into Rio Amazonas. Colombia: River Amazon.

Description
C. agassizii is reminiscent of *C. ambiacus* and each species has a very variable colour pattern that overlaps the other. The head and body is covered by numerous ill-defined brown spots, varying in size and density. Some specimens have a longitudinal series of spots that forms an irregular stripe on the junction of the body scutes on the posterior half of the body, which is margined by a pale yellow line – suggesting a trilineate pattern. In other specimens, this stripe is absent. The black pigment continues into the body on some specimens but not on others. There are 4–7 irregular bars in the caudal fin.

C. agassizii, *C. ambiacus* and *C. leopardus* occur sympatrically in some rivers. *C. leopardus* can easily be distinguished from the other 2 species by its dorsal fin blotch, which is isolated. Even ichthyologists find it difficult to distinguish between *C. agassizii* and *C. ambiacus*.

SIZE   The largest specimen examined was 55.6 mm, but this fish should grow to 70 mm in the aquarium.

Breeding
This species has been bred under aquarium conditions.

Corydoras amapaensis
Nijssen, 1972

Taxonomic Details
First collected by J. P. Gosse in 1962.

ETYMOLOGY   Named after the state of Amapá, where it was collected.

Distribution
Brazil: Amapá – Cachoera creek at right bank of Rio Amapari, Rio Amapari system and the Oyapock River system.

Description
C. amapaensis is very similar in colour pattern to several other long-snouted species (*C. semiaquilis*, *C. septentrionalis*, *C. solox* and *C. treitlii*). All these species exhibit a large blotch on the

Agassiz's Corydoras (*Corydoras agassizii*). Adult.

Corydoras amapaensis. Young adult. Adult coloration is reached in 8 weeks.

mid-side of the body, which in *C. amapaensis* varies in size, intensity of colour and distribution. (In *C. semiaquilus* it covers most of the body; in *C. septentrionalis* it is confined to below the dorsal fin; in *C. solox* it is narrow and wedge-shaped, confined to the upper body scutes, starting below the dorsal fin spine, and ending at the caudal peduncle; in *C. treitlii* it is wedge-shaped, starting behind the operculum and finishing at the caudal peduncle.) *C. amapaensis* has a feature known in only 2 other species of *Corydoras* (*C. octocirrus* and *C. septentrionalis*): it possesses 3 pairs of rictal barbels. In all other known species, there are only 2 pairs.

SIZE The largest specimen examined was 62.6 mm, but this fish should grow to 70 mm in the aquarium.

Breeding
This is possibly the first of the snouted *Corydoras* to be bred in captivity.

SPAWNING This took place after a 4°C temperature drop (from 23°C to 19°C). The eggs (approximately 1.5 mm diameter) were laid in spawning-mops and on the sides of the tank and hatched in 4 days.

FEEDING As for *C. acutus* (p. 39).

FRY Adult coloration was reached in 8 weeks.

Corydoras ambiacus
Cope, 1872
Black-spot Catfish

Taxonomic Details
First collected by J. Hauxwell.

SYNONYMS
C. grafi Holly, 1940
C. melanistius longirostris Hoedeman, 1952

Distribution
Ecuador: Napo – River Panayacu, Rio Yasuni, Quebrada to Rio Jatuncocha. Colombia: Rio Loreto – Yacu tributary of Rio Amazonas. Peru: Loreto – Rio Ampiacu, Pebus de Cano, Rio Nanay drainage, Menona Cocha, west of Iquitos; Rio Amazonas just north of Iquitos; Rio Yavari, Lago Matamata, Rio Javari, Vincente Cocha; Ucayali – Rio Tamaya system, Lamiria Cocha and Lobo Cocha near Masisea.

Description
C. ambiacus is reminiscent of *C. agassizii* and each species has a very variable colour pattern that overlaps the other. In each the head and body is covered by numerous ill-defined brown spots varying in size and density. Most specimens of *C. ambiacus* have irregular black markings, forming an indistinct stripe along the mid-line at the junction of the body scutes on the posterior half of the body. This stripe is margined above and below by an unpigmented area. Small greyish-brown spots are present on the head of some specimens and absent on others. In some specimens, the black blotch on the dorsal fin (which continues into the body and varies in density) covers the anterior 4 rays and membrane and reaches to the top of the fin. In other specimens it only covers 3 anterior rays and does not reach the top of the fin. There are 4–7 irregular vertical bars in the caudal fin.

C. ambiacus, *C. agassizii* and *C. leopardus* occur sympatrically in some rivers. *C. leopardus* can easily be distinguished from the other 2 species by its dorsal fin blotch, which is isolated. Even ichthyologists find it difficult to distinguish between *C. ambiacus* and *C. agassizii*.

SIZE The largest specimen examined was 53.3 mm, but this fish should grow to 65 mm in the aquarium.

Corydoras amphibelus
Cope, 1872

Taxonomic Details
First collected by J. Hauxwell and known from a single specimen.

Distribution
Peru: Loreto – Rio Ampiyacu near Pebas.

Description
SIZE   The largest specimen examined was 27.4 mm, but this fish should grow to 60 mm in the aquarium.

Corydoras approuaguensis
Nijssen & Isbrücker, 1983

Taxonomic Details
First collected in 1983 by P. Y. Le Bail.

ETYMOLOGY   Named after the River Approuague, where it was collected.

Distribution
French Guiana: River Approuague.

Description
SIZE   The largest specimen examined was 56.5 mm, but this fish should grow to 60 mm in the aquarium.

Corydoras araguaiaensis
Sands, 1990

Taxonomic Details
ETYMOLOGY   Named after the Rio Araguaia, where the fish was collected.

Distribution
Brazil: Rio Araguaia.

Description
C. araguaiaensis has a similar colour pattern to *C. haraldschultzi* and *C. sterbai* but lacks the orange colour in the pectoral and ventral fins. Like *C. haraldschultzi*, it has irregular black spots on the head (these are whitish in *C. sterbai*) and 5–7 irregular vertical bars on the caudal fin (4–8 in *C. sterbai*).

SIZE   The largest specimen examined was 35 mm, but this fish should grow to 60 mm in the aquarium.

Corydoras arcuatus
Elwin, 1939
Skunk Corydoras

Taxonomic Details
This fish was described from an aquarium specimen.

ETYMOLOGY   From the Latin *arcuatus* = 'bent like a bow', alluding to the dark stripe in the body.

Distribution
Peru: Loreto – Rio Pacaya, tributary to Rio Ucayali and Rio Yavari. Ecuador: Napo – Jatun Cocha, Rio Yasuni drainage, tributary to Rio Napo. Colombia: Rio Caqueta, Rio Amazonas/Solimões. Brazil: Amazonas – Rio Purus system, creek into Rio Ipixuna.

Description
C. arcuatus has a similar colour pattern to *C. narcissus* and both species occur sympatrically in some rivers. The 2 species can be separated by their slightly different colour pattern and morphometric characters. *C. arcuatus* has a more solid and sharply-defined body stripe, a short, rounded snout and grows to 50.5 mm. (In *C. narcissus* the body stripe often continues into

Black-spot Catfish (*Corydoras ambiacus*). Adult. This species is difficult to distinguish from *C. agassizii*.

Skunk Corydoras (*Corydoras arcuatus*). Adult. Adult coloration is reached in 10–12 weeks.

the lower lobe of the caudal fin, almost reaching the tip, the snout is long and acute, and a length of 64.7 mm may be reached.)

C. arcuatus seems to be a delicate species when first imported, but once settled into a tank it does very well.

SIZE   The largest specimen examined was 50.5 mm, but this fish should grow to 55 mm in the aquarium.

Breeding
SPAWNING   These fish usually spawn after a cold-water-change has reduced the temperature to 16°C from 21°C. They spawn in typical 'T' formation and lay eggs of approximately 1.75 mm diameter. The eggs are usually laid in Java Moss and take 3–4 days to hatch.

FEEDING   As with *C. acutus* (p. 39).

FRY   Adult coloration is reached in 10–12 weeks.

Corydoras armatus
(Günther, 1868)

Taxonomic Details
First collected in 1808 by E. Bartlett.

ETYMOLOGY   From the Latin *armatus* = 'armed', alluding to the dorsal fin spine.

SYNONYMS   *Callichthys armatus* Günther, 1868

Distribution
Peru: Loreto – Rio Huallaga and Rio Yavari (a river which borders Brazil where it is named Rio Javari).

Description
C. armatus is reminiscent of *C. loretoensis* in colour pattern, but differs in a number of morphometric characters: body depth and width, length of dorsal and pectoral fin spines, snout length and depth of caudal peduncle. The body is covered with small dark-brown spots, widely distributed in an irregular pattern. (In *C. loretoensis* the spots are larger and darker.) The dorsal fin spine has a grey pigment whilst the remainder of the dorsal fin and all other fins are hyaline, apart from some specimens which had a small brownish blotch on the top of the adipose fin membrane.

C. armatus and *C. loretoensis* occur sympatrically in some rivers. *C. armatus* is easily distinguished from other *Corydoras* spp. by its long dorsal fin spine.

SIZE   The largest specimen examined was 48.4 mm, but this fish should grow to 50 mm in the aquarium.

Corydoras atropersonatus
Weitzman & Nijssen, 1970

Taxonomic Details
First collected in 1960 by R. Ollala.

ETYMOLOGY   From the Latin *atropersonatus* = 'with a black mask', alluding to the mask across the eyes.

Distribution
Ecuador: Pastaza – Rio Conambo at the mouth of Rio Shione, Rio Tigre system and Rio Shione Yacu near the confluence with Rio Conambo. Peru: Loreto – Rio Nanay and Rio Ampiyacu system.

Description
C. atropersonatus has a similar colour pattern to *C. sychri* but in *C. atropersonatus* the spots on the body are larger and fewer. The 2 species also

Corydoras armatus. Young adult. This species is easily recognized by its long dorsal fin spine.

Corydoras atropersonatus. Juvenile.

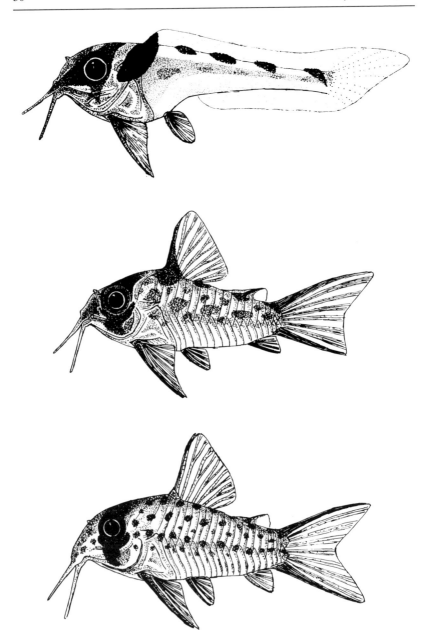

Corydoras atropersonatus. Growth stages. From top to bottom: fry at 7 days; young fish at 4–6 weeks; young fish at 10–12 weeks.

differ in a number of morphometric characters: body width, snout length and the number of lateral body scutes.

C. atropersonatus does not travel very well. When first imported, it seems to be extremely delicate, but if you can get it through the first couple of weeks, and slowly acclimatize it, it settles in quite nicely.

SIZE The largest specimen examined was 43.7 mm, but these fish should grow to 50 mm in the aquarium.

Breeding
FISH USED 1 male, 30 mm. 1 female, 32 mm. These were both wild-caught specimens.

BREEDING-TANK 45 cm × 20 cm × 15 cm deep, furnished with one box-filter and a small clump of Java Moss.

WATER Tap water that had been standing for 2 weeks; 24°C, pH 7.02, 6°GH.

SPAWNING The spawning took place in typical 'T' formation 2 days after a partial water-change had reduced the temperature to 20°C. A total of 80 eggs were laid in groups of 3–5. The eggs were approximately 1.5 mm in diameter. The adults were removed before the spawning was completed as they had reached a point where they were eating more eggs than they were laying!
Once the adults had been removed, the water was treated with methylene blue to prevent the infertile eggs from contaminating the fertile ones. After 4 days the eggs hatched and the fry were free-swimming 2 days later.

FEEDING As for *C. acutus* (p. 39).

FRY Size at: 7 days – 4 mm; 1 month – 8.5 mm; 2 months – 13 mm; 3 months – 21 mm.

Corydoras aurofrenatus
Eigenmann & Kennedy, 1903

Taxonomic Details
First collected in 1900 by J. P. Anisits and described from a single specimen.

ETYMOLOGY From the Latin *aurum* = 'gold' and *frenatum* = 'bridled'.

Distribution
Paraguay: Rio Aguada, a tributary of the Rio Aquido Canigi.

Description
SIZE The largest specimen examined was 40.9 mm, but this fish should grow to 55 mm in the aquarium.

Corydoras axelrodi
Rössel, 1962b
Banded Corydoras

Taxonomic Details
First collected by K. Swegles.

ETYMOLOGY Named in honour of Dr Herbert Axelrod.

Distribution
Colombia: Rio Meta and Rio Manacacias.

Description
C. axelrodi has a similar colour pattern to *C. loxozonus*: both have a conspicuous, dark, oblique stripe on the body which occurs just above the junction of the body scutes in *C. axelrodi* and just below the dorsal fin in *C. loxozonus*; both have a mask across the eye. *C. axelrodi* has scattered pigment below the body stripe, forming 1 or 2 irregular horizontal stripes (3–5 in *C. loxozonus*), and the dorsal and caudal fins are clear (those of *C. loxozonus* have scattered pigment).

These fish do not travel very well. When they are first imported they are rather delicate and take some time to settle down. Once they are established in a tank they seem to be quite hardy.

SIZE The largest specimen examined was 35.9 mm, but this fish should grow to 45 mm in the aquarium.

Breeding
SPAWNING This usually takes place after a cold-water-change has lowered the temperature to 20°C from 24°C. Spawning followed the typical 'T' pattern and eggs of approximately 1.8 mm diameter were laid singly in a nylon spawning-mop. The eggs took 4 days to hatch.

FEEDING As for *C. acutus* (p. 39).

FRY Adult coloration was reached in 10–12 weeks.

Corydoras baderi
Geisler, 1969

Taxonomic Details
First collected in 1967 by R. Geisler.

ETYMOLOGY Named in honour of Mr Bader.

Distribution
Brazil: Pará – Rio Paru de Oeste. Surinam: Marowijne – Marowijne River system, creek at left bank of Oelemari River.

Description
SIZE The largest specimen examined was 46.8 mm, but this fish should grow to 50 mm in the aquarium.

Corydoras axelrodi. Juvenile. Adult coloration is reached in 10–12 weeks.

Corydoras barbatus
(Quoy & Gaimard, 1824)
Bearded Corydoras

Taxonomic Details

ETYMOLOGY   From the Latin *barbatus* = 'bearded', alluding to the bristles on the cheeks of adult males.

SYNONYMS
Callichthys barbatus Quoy & Gaimard, 1824
Corydoras kronei A. de Miranda Ribeiro, 1907
C. eigenmanni Von Ihering, 1907

Distribution

Brazil: Rio de Janeiro and São Paulo.

Description

C. barbatus is one of the species of *Corydoras* that exhibits sexual dimorphism. In adult males the front of the pre-operculum is margined with bristles. (These are absent in females). Only one other known species of *Corydoras* shares this feature: adult males of *C. macropterus*. Males can also be distinguished from females by their longer pectoral fin spines and extended soft dorsal fin rays.

C. barbatus shows a great variation in colour pattern. In São Paulo, it is found in the blackwater streams, where the water is clear (but tea-coloured) and flows over sandy or sand-and-pebble substrate; the specimens from this area exhibit an intense coloration. Specimens that are found in the whitewaters of Rio de Janeiro are much paler in colour.

C. barbatus are the largest examined species of *Corydoras* at 72.3 mm with *C. robustus* coming in a close second at 71.2 mm.

[The specimen in the photograph on p. 54 came from the USA in 1975; unfortunately we only received 1 male.

I have never seen male aquarium specimens that were exhibiting the bristles on the cheeks. I have only seen them on preserved specimens in the museum in Amsterdam.]

SIZE   The largest specimen examined was 72.3 mm, but this fish should grow to 80 mm in the aquarium.

Breeding

FISH USED   2 males, 50 mm. 2 females, 55 mm.

BREEDING-TANK   45 cm × 30 cm × 30 cm, furnished with a 1.5 cm layer of well-washed river sand, 1 box-filter containing peat and filter wool, and 4 floating spawning-mops made from nylon wool and suspended from pieces of polystyrene. The mops had been boiled before use to remove any dyes.

WATER   Tap water that had been standing for 2 weeks; 21°C, pH 7.6, 10°GH.

SPAWNING   The spawning occurred in a slight variation of the typical 'T' formation. The actual mating-clinch only lasted for a few seconds and, when the female was ready, she drove into the side of the male, forcing him against the side of the tank. They then parted and sank to the bottom of the tank where the female leaned over on one pectoral fin and made a paddling motion with the other.

At this point, eggs were released (2–6) into her ventral fins which were clasped together to form a pouch. Once she had recovered, she then moved off to deposit the eggs. These were all placed on top of each other. When all the eggs have been laid they look very much like a small bunch of grapes. Altogether 87 eggs were laid, each approximately 1.65 mm in diameter.

After spawning was completed, the adults were moved to another tank to

Bearded Corydoras (*Corydoras barbatus*). Young adult. When fully grown, males can be distinguished from females by their longer pectoral fin spines, extended dorsal fin rays and the bristles on the pre-operculum.

be reconditioned and the eggs were treated with methylene blue to prevent unfertilized eggs contaminating the fertile ones. The day after spawning, all the eggs were seen to be fertile and, 3 days later, the fry started to emerge from the eggs. It then became obvious that there was a problem. On closer inspection it could be seen that the fry were having difficulty breaking through the egg membrane. In subsequent spawnings this was cured by adding phosphoric acid to the tank water (at a rate of 10 ml per 9 l) after the adults had been removed, thus reducing the pH to 6.2 and the GH to 6°. This had the effect of helping the egg membrane to break down so that the fry could break through without becoming exhausted, thereby giving them a better start in life. After several spawnings, this treatment was not

needed because the females seemed to produce eggs that were better matched to the water conditions in which they were being kept, so that the fry were able to emerge unaided.

When the fry emerged they were 3 mm long and they became free-swimming in 2 days (after they had absorbed their yolk sac).

FEEDING Fry were fed as for *C. acutus* (p. 39) in the early stages. As they grew larger they were fed on a mixture of grated beef heart mixed with a little Bemax and spinach. (This mixture was blended together and then frozen, making it easy to scrape off small amounts when needed.)

FRY Size at: 7 days – 5 mm; 1 month – 14 mm; 2 months – 26 mm. Adult coloration was reached in 6–8 weeks.

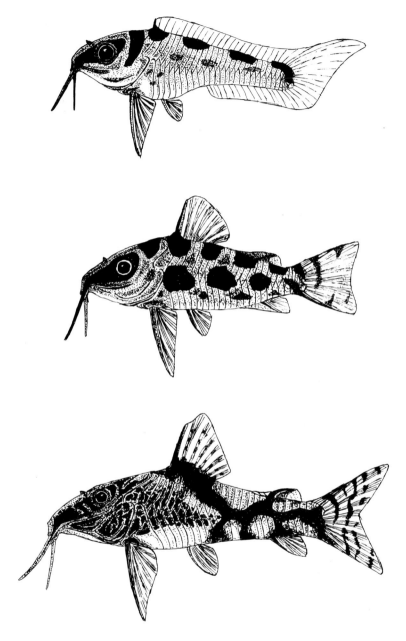

Corydoras barbatus. Growth stages. From top to bottom: fry at 7 days; young fish at 4 weeks; young fish at 8 weeks.

Corydoras bicolor
Nijssen & Isbrücker, 1967

Taxonomic Details
First collected in 1961 by H. P. Pijpers.

ETYMOLOGY From the Latin *bi* = 'two' or 'double', and *color* = 'tint' or 'hue', alluding to the 2 colours this fish shows.

Distribution
Surinam: Nickerie – Corantijn River system, Sipaliwini River near the border with Brazil.

Description
C. bicolour is closely related to *C. melanistius melanistius* but lacks the pigment spots on the head and body.

SIZE The largest specimen examined was 30.4 mm, but this fish should grow to 45 mm in the aquarium.

Corydoras bifasciatus
Nijssen, 1972

Taxonomic Details
First collected in 1964 by J. P. Gosse.

ETYMOLOGY From the Latin *bi* = 'two' or 'double' and *fasciatus* = 'striped', alluding to the 2 stripes on the body.

Distribution
Brazil: Pará – creek at the left bank of Rio Cururu, tributary of Upper Rio Tapajos.

Description
SIZE The largest specimen examined was 51.5 mm, but this fish should grow to 55 mm in the aquarium.

Corydoras blochi blochi. Adult. This subspecies can be distinguished from *C. b. vittatus* by the mask across the eyes and the longer pectoral fin spine.

Corydoras blochi blochi
Nijssen, 1971

Taxonomic Details
First collected in 1968 by E. Ledecky-Janacek.

ETYMOLOGY Named in honour of Dr M. E. Bloch, a famous German ichthyologist. In 1794 he described *Cataphractus punctatus* which is now *Corydoras punctatus*, the type species of the genus *Corydoras*.

Distribution
Guyana: Essequibo – Moco Moco creek, tributary of Rio Catuca, Rio Branco system, Essequibo River system. Venezuela: Rio Orinoco system. Brazil: Rio Branco system.

Description
C. b. blochi differs from the subspecies *C. b. vittatus* in colour pattern. *C. b. blochi* has a mask across the eyes and a caudal fin bearing 6–10 irregular vertical bars (both features are absent in *C. b. vittatus*). It lacks the pigment at the junction of the body scutes which, in *C. b. vittatus*, forms a mid-lateral line from the caudal peduncle to about halfway below the dorsal fin but has a longer pectoral fin spine.

SIZE The largest specimen examined was 47.5 mm, but this fish should grow to 60 mm in the aquarium.

Breeding
This species has been bred under aquarium conditions.

Corydoras blochi vittatus
Nijssen, 1971

Taxonomic Details
First collected in 1913 by J. D. Haseman.

ETYMOLOGY From the Latin *vittatus* referring to the stripe at the junction of the body scutes.

Distribution
Brazil: Maranho – tributary of Rio Itapicuru at Caxias.

Description
C. b. vittatus can be distinguished from *C. b. blochi* by the absence of a mask across the eyes and of vertical bars on the caudal fin. It also has a shorter pectoral fin spine and the pigment at the junction of the body scutes forms a mid-lateral line from the caudal peduncle to about half-way below the dorsal fin.

SIZE The largest specimen examined was 44.4 mm, but this fish should grow to 60 mm in the aquarium.

Corydoras boehlkei
Nijssen & Isbrücker, 1982

Taxonomic Details
First collected in 1977 by Dr James E. Boehlke and W. G. Saul.

ETYMOLOGY Named in honour of Dr James E. Boehlke.

Distribution
Venezuela: Rio Cuchime.

Description
C. boehlkei resembles *C. leucomelas* but both vary slightly in colour pattern. The pigment on the dorsal fin spine and first 2 rays (including the membrane) forms a wedge-shaped blotch. (In some specimens of *C. leucomelas* all the dorsal fin except the last ray is black; in others the black area is smaller and the pigment extends on to the body.) There are isolated spots on

the body and no pigment over the eyes. (In some *C. leucomelas* the spots join to form irregular lines and there is a bold black mask.) Unlike *C. leucomelas*, there is no barring on the caudal fin.

SIZE   The largest specimen examined was 25.7 mm, but this fish should grow to 55 mm in the aquarium.

but it is a much more robust species and the reticulated colour pattern extends into the ventral region. All the fins are heavily pigmented but the dorsal fin blotch, present in *C. reticulatus*, is absent.

SIZE   The largest specimen examined was 58.1 mm, but this fish should grow to 65 mm in the aquarium.

Corydoras boesmani
Nijssen & Isbrücker, 1967

Taxonomic Details
First collected in 1964 by Dr Boesman.

ETYMOLOGY   Named in honour of Dr Boesman.

Distribution
Surinam: Brokopondo – Suriname River system, little tributaries of Gran Rio between Ligorio and Awaradam Falls and the Corantijn River system.

Description
SIZE   The largest specimen examined was 42 mm, but this fish should grow to 45 mm in the aquarium.

Corydoras bolivianus
Nijssen & Isbrücker, 1983

Taxonomic Details
First collected in 1982 by G. Loubens.

ETYMOLOGY   Named after Bolivia, the country where the fish was collected.

Distribution
Bolivia: Beni – Rio Mamore.

Description
C. bolivianus shares the same colour pattern as *C. sodalis* and *C. reticulatus*

Corydoras bondi bondi
Gosline, 1940

Taxonomic Details
First collected in 1939 by F. F. Bond.

ETYMOLOGY   Named after F. F. Bond.

SYNONYMS   *C. punctatus sipaliwini* Hoedeman, 1965

Distribution
Venezuela: Bolivar – Rio Yuruari, Rio Carichapo, tributary of Rio Yuruari. Surinam: Sipaliwini River, Corantijn River system, Marowijne River system.

Description
C. b. bondi differs principally from *C. b. coppenamensis* in its colour pattern which consists of irregularly-formed spots on the head and body (mainly confined to the upper body) that sometimes join together. The line at the junction of the body scutes is slightly zigzag. (In *C. b. coppenamensis*, the spots are circular and the black line is usually well defined.)

SIZE   The largest specimen examined was 45.9 mm, but this fish should grow to 50 mm in the aquarium.

Breeding
SPAWNING   These fish breed in typical 'T' formation and lay their eggs anywhere. Eggs hatch in 4–5 days.

Corydoras bondi bondi. Adult. Note the irregularly-formed spots and zigzag line at the junction of the body scutes.

FEEDING As for *C. acutus* (p. 39).

FRY Adult coloration is reached in 8 weeks. Juveniles often look like *C. bondi coppenamensis* until their pigmentation develops and they mature.

Corydoras bondi coppenamensis
Nijssen, 1970

Taxonomic Details
First collected in 1967 by Dr Han Nijssen.

ETYMOLOGY Named after the Coppename River, where it was discovered.

Distribution
Surinam: Saramacca – Coppename River, creek at the left bank of Coppename River, Corantijn River system, Palomev River and Rupununi River.

Description
C. b. coppenamensis differs principally from *C. b. bondi* in its colour pattern although it also has a smaller eye and a shorter dorsal fin spine. It has circular spots on the head and body and the black line at the junction of the body scutes is usually well defined. (In *C. b. bondi* the spots are irregularly formed, sometimes joining together, and are mainly confined to the upper body. Also the mid-lateral line is slightly zigzag.)

SIZE The largest specimen examined was 45 mm, but this fish should grow to 50 mm in the aquarium.

Breeding
This species has been known to breed under aquarium conditions.

Corydoras burgessi
Axelrod, 1987

Taxonomic Details
First collected by Adolfo Schwartz.

ETYMOLOGY Named in honour of Dr Warren E. Burgess.

Distribution
Brazil: Amazonas – Rio Unini.

Corydoras bondi coppenamensis. Adult. Note the circular spots and well-defined line at the junction of the body scutes.

Description
SIZE The largest specimen examined was 49.3 mm, but this fish should grow to 60 mm in the aquarium.

Corydoras carlae
Nijssen & Isbrücker, 1983

Taxonomic Details
First collected in 1977 by J. P. Gosse.

ETYMOLOGY Named in honour of Carla Lindenaar-Sparrius.

Distribution
Argentina: Rio Iguaza.

Description
SIZE The largest specimen examined was 41.8 mm, but this fish should grow to 50 mm in the aquarium.

Corydoras caudimaculatus
Rossel, 1961
Tail-spot Corydoras

Taxonomic Details
First collected by H. Schultz.

ETYMOLOGY From the Latin *cauda* = 'tail' and *maculatus* = 'spotted', alluding to the spot in the caudal peduncle.

Distribution
Brazil: Rondônia – main stream of upper Rio Guapore.

Description
SIZE The largest specimen examined was 39.3 mm, but this fish should grow to 45 mm in the aquarium.

Corydoras cervinus
Rossel, 1962

Taxonomic Details
First collected by H. Schultz.

ETYMOLOGY From the Latin *cervinus* = 'deer'.

Distribution
Brazil: Rondônia – main stream of upper Rio Guapore.

Description
SIZE The largest specimen examined was 49.4 mm, but this fish should grow to 60 mm in the aquarium.

Corydoras cochui
Myers & Weitzman, 1954

Taxonomic Details
First collected in 1953 by F. Cochu.

ETYMOLOGY Named in honour of F. Cochu.

Distribution
Brazil: Goiás – Rio Araguaua.

Description
C. cochui is a pygmy species with a colour pattern similar to that of *C. habrosus*. It can be distinguished by the stripe along the mid-side of the body, which forms 4–5 irregular-shaped blotches (2–3 in *C. habrosus*) and the absence of a black spot at the base of the anal fin.

SIZE The largest specimen examined was 25.7 mm, but this fish should grow to 35 mm in the aquarium.

Corydoras concolor
Weitzman, 1961

Taxonomic Details
First collected in 1946 by A. Fernandez-Yepez.

ETYMOLOGY From the Latin *concolor* = 'uniform colour'.

Distribution
Venezuela: Rio Parguaza, a stream flowing into the Rio Orinoco.

Description
C. concolor slightly resembles some colour varieties of *C. aeneus*, but differs in many other characters. The body depth is much greater, the dorsal fin spine is much longer and the eye is much larger. Its most characteristic feature is the lack of heavy dark marks, blotches, bars or lines. *C. concolor* should not be confused with any other known species of *Corydoras*.

SIZE The largest specimen examined was 54.2 mm, but this fish should grow to 55 mm in the aquarium.

Corydoras condiscipulus
Nijssen & Isbrücker, 1980

Taxonomic Details
First collected in 1962 by J. P. Gosse.

ETYMOLOGY From the Latin *condiscipulus* = 'schoolmate', alluding to the sympatric occurrence of this species with *C. oiapoquensis* with which it shares its colour pattern.

Distribution
French Guiana: Cumuri creek at the left bank of Oyapock River, upstream of first rapids of Grande Roche, and in the Oyapock River system.

Description
SIZE The largest specimen examined was 54.4 mm, but this fish should grow to 55 mm in the aquarium.

Corydoras copei
Nijssen & Isbrucker, 1986

Taxonomic Details
First collected in 1976 by C. Heyer.

ETYMOLOGY Named in honour of Mr Cope.

Distribution
Peru: Loreto – lower course of Rio Huytoyacu, right bank tributary to Rio Pastaza.

Corydoras concolor. Adult.

Corydoras delphax. Juvenile. The colour pattern in this species is extremely variable.

Description

SIZE The largest specimen examined was 39.3 mm, but this fish should grow to 55 mm in the aquarium.

Corydoras cortesi
Castro, 1987

Taxonomic Details
First collected in 1982 by J. Medina.

ETYMOLOGY Named in honour of Dr Abdon Cortes Lombana.

Distribution
Colombia: Rio Arauca, near to Arauca.

Description
SIZE The largest specimen examined was 39.9 mm, but this fish should grow to 60 mm in the aquarium.

Corydoras davidsandsi
Black, 1987

Taxonomic Details
ETYMOLOGY Named in honour of D. D. Sands.

Distribution
Brazil: Tapuruguara – Rio Inambu.

Description
SIZE The largest specimen examined was 44 mm, but this fish should grow to 65 mm in the aquarium.

Breeding
This fish has been known to have bred under aquarium conditions.

Corydoras delphax
Nijssen & Isbrücker, 1983

Taxonomic Details
First collected in 1972 by T. Hongslo.

ETYMOLOGY From the Greek *delphax* = 'young pig', alluding to its feeding behaviour.

Distribution
Colombia: Rio Orinoco and Rio Inrida system.

Description
C. delphax has an extremely variable colour pattern. The amount of pigment on the body (including the extension of the blotch in the dorsal fin) varies in size and distribution. It can form narrow lines confined to the margins of the scutes or irregular small spots on the scutes. In some specimens the dorsal fin spine, the first 3 soft rays and the membrane are black up to the tip and the remainder of the soft rays have scattered pigment. In some specimens, the spots on the caudal fin are conspicuous, arranged into irregular vertical bars. In others they are less prominent.

SIZE The largest specimen examined was 57.2 mm, but this fish should grow to 75 mm in the aquarium.

Corydoras ehrhardti
Steindachner, 1910

Taxonomic Details
First collected in 1909 by W. W. Ehrhardt.

ETYMOLOGY Named in honour of W. W. Ehrhardt.

SYNONYMS *C. meridionalis* Von Ihering, 1911

Corydoras ehrhardti. Adult.

Distribution
Brazil: Santa Catarina – affluents from Jaragua mountains near Joinville.

Description
C. ehrhardti is sometimes confused with *C. paleatus*, but has a different colour pattern and body shape. The body is less deep and there are 2 distinct blotches on the body, one below the dorsal fin spine and the other below the adipose fin; the remaining parts of body (except for the ventral region) are lightly pigmented, apart from the head which is dark. (*C. paleatus* has 3 blotches on the body: one below the dorsal fin, one below the adipose fin spine and the third on the caudal peduncle. The remaining parts of the body and head, except for the ventral region, have irregularly scattered heavy pigment.)
[The fish in the photograph above was purchased 18 years ago from a shop in London. It was in a tank full of *C. paleatus*. The owner of the shop thought I was mad for wanting 'the badly-coloured *C. paleatus*' when there were better-coloured fish in the tank!]

SIZE The largest specimen examined was 47.4 mm, but this fish should grow to 50 mm in the aquarium.

Corydoras elegans
Steindachner, 1877
Elegant Corydoras

Taxonomic Details
First collected in 1865 by the Thayer Expedition, but not really known to European aquarists until the 1930s.

ETYMOLOGY From the Latin *elegans* = 'tasteful' or 'fine'.

SYNONYMS *C. pestai* Holly, 1940

Distribution
Peru: Loreto – Rio Ucayali, Rio Ampiyacu, Rio Nanay drainage, Rio Yavari and Rio Tamaya. Brazil: Amazonas – Rio Solimões. Ecuador: Napo – Rio Lagartococha, northern tributary to Rio Aguarico and Rio Napo drainage. Colombia: Rio Caqueta, Rio Amazonas/Solimões.

Description

C. elegans is often confused with *C. napoensis*. Apart from the differences in morphometric characters, there are differences in the colour patterns. *C. elegans* has a very variable pattern which is different in each sex, the colour of the male being more intense than that of the female. It is also one of those species in which the female grows larger than the male. The dorsal fin has an irregular-shaped pattern (adult males of *C. napoensis* have a large black blotch on the dorsal fin) and the short, round snout is an easily-recognized feature. This species has occasionally been seen to feed and swim in mid-water, in a very similar fashion to *C. hastatus*.

C. elegans and *C. napoensis* occur sympatrically in Ecuador and Peru.

SIZE   The largest specimen examined was 46.4 mm, but this fish should grow to 55 mm in the aquarium (males to 50 mm).

Breeding

FISH USED   3 males, 35 mm, 2 females, 40 mm. These were all wild-caught fish.

BREEDING-TANK   45 cm × 20 cm × 15 cm deep. This was furnished with a 1 cm layer of fine, 2 mm diameter gravel and 1 box-filter.

WATER   Tap water that had been standing for 2 weeks, 21°C, pH 7, 11°GH.

SPAWNING   These were one of the few *Corydoras* observed spawning that did not follow the normal 'T' pattern. To begin with there was a tremendous amount of cleaning activity in the tank, especially around the top 5 cm. Such was their vigour, the fish occasionally came right out of the water. Once they had decided everything was clean enough, or so it seemed, one of the females (who was particularly heavy with roe) started to pester each male in turn, nudging them in the side. After a short time, one of the males started to take notice and both fish started circling each other (just like cichlids do when sizing each other up before a fight). After a while they stopped and settled on the bottom, sitting up on their ventral fins and facing each other. After another 10 seconds or so, they separated, swimming off in opposite directions.

Elegant Corydoras (*Corydoras elegans*). Adult. The male is slightly smaller than the female but is more intensely coloured.

Corydoras elegans. Growth stages. From top to bottom: fry at 7 days; young fish at 4 weeks; young fish at 8–10 weeks.

The female then started cleaning one particular part of the tank wall very vigorously before returning to the centre of the tank and perching on her ventral fins, which were clamped together to form a pouch. She then deposited a cluster of eggs into this pouch and laid them on the previously-cleaned site about 1.5 cm from the surface of the water. During this time both males had carried on cleaning and, whenever they came to the eggs, hovered over them for a few seconds and then carried on. This activity went on until over 250 eggs were laid. The eggs were approximately 1 mm in diameter. The female placed the eggs in batches of 15–20. As this was the second spawning, the adult fish were left in the tank with the eggs to see if they would eat them. They took no interest in them at all.

The water was treated with methylene blue to stop any infertile eggs from contaminating the good ones. The fertility rate was about 65 per cent. The eggs started to hatch after 3 days and, at this stage, the adult fish were removed from the tank. The eggs all hatched by the fourth day and the fry were free-swimming 2 days later.

FEEDING   As for *C. acutus* (p. 39).

FRY   Size at: 7 days – 4.5 mm; 1 month – 7.5 mm; 2 months – 12 mm; 3 months – 18.5 mm.

Corydoras ellisae
Gosline, 1940

Taxonomic Details
First collected in 1909 by J. D. Haseman.

Distribution
Paraguay: Arroyo Pona – Rio Paraguay system near Asunción.

Description
SIZE   The largest specimen examined was 47.7 mm, but this fish should grow to 65 mm in the aquarium.

Corydoras ephippifer
Nijssen, 1972

Taxonomic Details
First collected in 1962 by J. P. Gosse.

ETYMOLOGY   From the Latin *ephippos* = 'mounted as though on a horse'!

Distribution
Brazil: Amapá – Cachoeira creek at the right bank of Rio Amapari and in the Rio Amapari system.

Description
SIZE   The largest specimen examined was 49.3 mm, but this fish should grow to 50 mm in the aquarium.

Corydoras eques
Steindachner, 1877

Taxonomic Details
First collected in 1865 by the Thayer Expedition.

ETYMOLOGY   From the Latin *equus* = 'a horse'.

Distribution
Brazil: Amazonas – Rio Amazonas at Codajas.

Description
SIZE   The largest specimen examined was 47.8 mm, but this fish should grow to 50 mm in the aquarium.

Corydoras esperanzae
Castro, 1987

Taxonomic Details
First collected in 1984 by Dario M. Castro.

ETYMOLOGY Named in honour of Esperanza Rocha.

Distribution
Colombia: Cano Orocue – Rio Meta.

Description
SIZE The largest specimen examined was 50.8 mm, but this fish should grow to 55 mm in the aquarium.

Corydoras evelynae
Rossel, 1963

Taxonomic Details
First collected in 1962 by Dr H. R. Axelrod.

ETYMOLOGY Named in honour of Evelyn Axelrod.

Distribution
Brazil: Amazonas – upper Rio Solimões.

Description
SIZE The largest specimen examined was 40.6 mm, but this fish should grow to 65 mm in the aquarium.

Corydoras filamentosus
Nijssen & Isbrücker, 1983

Taxonomic Details
First collected in 1980 by R. P. Vari.

ETYMOLOGY From the Latin *filamentosus* = 'filament-like', alluding to the extended rays on the dorsal fin.

Distribution
Surinam: Nickerie – Corantijn River system.

Description
SIZE The largest specimen examined was 31.5 mm, but this fish should grow to 50 mm in the aquarium.

Corydoras flaveolus
R. Von Ihering, 1911

Taxonomic Details
First collected in 1906 by R. Von Ihering.

Distribution
Brazil: São Paulo – tributaries of Rio Piracicaba.

Description
SIZE The largest specimen examined was 33.6 mm, but this fish should grow to 55 mm in the aquarium.

Corydoras fowleri
Boehlke, 1950

Taxonomic Details
First collected in 1941 by W. G. Scherer.

ETYMOLOGY Named in honour of Dr Henry W. Fowler.

Distribution
Peru: Loreto – Cano del Chancho, upper Pebas, Rio Amazonas system.

Description
This species is compared with *C. treitlii* on p. 117.

SIZE The largest specimen examined was 65.6 mm, but this fish should grow to 70 mm in the aquarium.

Corydoras garbei
R. Von Ihering, 1911
Honey Corydoras

Taxonomic Details
First collected in 1908 by E. Garbe.

ETYMOLOGY Named in honour of E. Garbe.

Distribution
Brazil: Bahia – Rio São Francisco and Rio Granjeiro.

Description
C. garbei should not be mistaken for any other *Corydorus* species because it has a unique colour pattern. The dorsal fin always has a broad, brown, horizontal bar just below the tip. The pigment is mostly confined to the rays. The brown pigment in the caudal fin forms 3–5 broad, irregular, vertical bars.

SIZE The largest specimen examined was 34.4 mm, but this fish should grow to 50 mm in the aquarium.

Breeding
FISH USED 3 males, 35 mm. 1 female, 38 mm. These were all wild-caught fish.

BREEDING-TANK 45 cm × 30 cm × 30 cm deep, furnished with a 1.5 cm layer of fine gravel, 1 box-filter, 4 nylon spawning-mops and a large clump of Java Moss.

WATER Tap water that had been standing for 2 weeks and was 20 cm deep; 21°C, pH 7.6, 14°GH.

SPAWNING The fish were placed in the tank during the evening. Next morning 30 per cent of the water was changed, being replaced with pre-conditioned water which lowered the pH from 7.6 to 6. (This was achieved by adding phosphoric acid to the replacement water at a rate of 10 ml per 9 l.)

Mating followed that evening in the typical *Corydoras* 'T' formation. Only 12 eggs were laid, approximately 2.5 mm diameter. (All subsequent spawnings also produced small numbers of eggs – the largest number laid was 16.) All the eggs proved to be fertile and the fry started to emerge from them after 4 days. They were free-swimming 2 days later.

FEEDING As for *C. acutus* (p. 39).

FRY Size at: 7 days – 6 mm; 1 month – 11 mm; 2 months – 16.5 mm; 3 months – 19 mm. Adult coloration was reached in 4–6 weeks.

NOTE *C. garbei* was found to be a very shy and retiring species, and therefore needed plenty of cover in the breeding-tank. This caused problems because, although the fish spawned readily in Java Moss, it was difficult to observe the spawning. These fish turned out to be avid egg-eaters, which probably accounts for the small number of eggs!

Corydoras geryi
Nijssen & Isbrücker, 1983

Taxonomic Details
First collected in 1982 by G. Loubens.

ETYMOLOGY Named in honour of Dr Jaques Robert Géry.

Distribution
Bolivia: Beni – Rio Mamore.

Description
SIZE The largest specimen examined was 41.1 mm, but this fish should grow to 50 mm in the aquarium.

Corydoras garbei. Growth stages. From top to bottom: fry at 4 days; young fish at 3 weeks; young fish at 6 weeks.

Corydoras gomezi
Castro, 1986

Taxonomic Details
First collected in 1984 by D. M. Castro. *C. gomezi* is known from a single specimen.

ETYMOLOGY Named in honour of Dr Juan Antonio Gomez.

Distribution
Colombia: Rio Amazonas, Solimões near Leticia.

Description
SIZE The largest specimen examined was 37.4 mm, but this fish should grow to 65 mm in the aquarium.

Corydoras gossei
Nijssen, 1972

Taxonomic Details
First collected in 1949 by C. Kalinowski.

ETYMOLOGY Named in honour of J. P. Gosse who has collected many specimens of *Corydoras*.

Distribution
Brazil: Rondônia – creek near Guajara Mirim, Rio Vilcanota system.

Description
SIZE The largest specimen examined was 55.1 mm, but this fish should grow to 55 mm in the aquarium.

Corydoras gracilis
Nijssen & Isbrücker, 1976

Taxonomic Details
First collected in 1975 by H. Baensch and H. Bleher.

ETYMOLOGY From the Latin *gracilis* = 'graceful' or 'slender'.

Distribution
Brazil: Amazonas – Rio Juana, tributary at right bank of Rio Aripuana, Rio Madeira basin.

Description
SIZE The largest specimen examined was 23.3 mm, but this fish should grow to 45 mm in the aquarium.

Corydoras griseus
Holly, 1940
Grey Corydoras

Taxonomic Details
C. griseus was described from an aquarium specimen.

ETYMOLOGY From the Latin *griseus* = 'grey', alluding to the colour of the species.

Distribution
Guyana: Essequibo – Potaro River.

Description
SIZE The largest specimen examined was 38.3 mm, but this fish should grow to 50 mm in the aquarium.

Corydoras guapore
Knaack, 1961

Taxonomic Details
First collected by H. Schultz.

ETYMOLOGY Named after Rio Guapore, where the fish was collected.

Distribution
Brazil: Rondônia – main stream of upper Rio Guapore.

Description

SIZE The largest specimen examined was 33.3 mm, but this species should grow to 45 mm in the aquarium.

Corydoras guianensis
Nijssen, 1970

Taxonomic Details
First collected in 1967 by Dr Han Nijssen.

ETYMOLOGY Named after the Guianas.

Distribution
Surinam: Nickerie – creek at right bank of Nickerie River, Coppename River and the Saramacco River.

Description
SIZE The largest specimen examined was 53 mm, but this species should grow to 55 mm in the aquarium.

Corydoras habrosus
Weitzman, 1960
Dainty Corydoras

Taxonomic Details
First collected in 1950 by A. Fernandez-Yepez.

ETYMOLOGY From the Greek *habros* = 'pretty', 'delicate' or 'dainty'.

Distribution
Venezuela: Cojedes – Rio Salinas, tributary of Rio Pao Viejo, El Baul. Colombia: Rio Casanare.

Description
C. habrosus seems to be closely related to *C. cochui*. Both seem to be a pygmy species and share a similar colour pattern. In *C. habrosus* the stripe along the mid-side of the robust body can be separated to form 2 or 3 irregular-shaped blotches and there is no black spot at the base of the anal fin. There are also 2–3 well-developed lateral-line pores above the coracoid, which are also present in several other species of *Corydoras*. In contrast, *C. cochui* is slender-bodied, the stripe can be separated into 4–5 blotches, and there is a black spot at the base of the anal fin.

I would not be surprised if, at a later date, a further revision of this genus is undertaken, and these 2 species were found to be synonymous.

SIZE The largest specimen examined was 20.7 mm, but this fish should grow to 35 mm in the aquarium. This is one of the few species in which the female grows larger than the male.

Breeding
FISH USED 4 males, 24 mm. 4 females, 30 mm. These were all wild-caught fish.

BREEDING-TANK 20 cm × 20 xm × 20 cm deep, furnished with a 1.2 cm layer of well-washed river sand, 1 box-filter and a small clump of Java Moss.

WATER Tap water that had been standing for 2 weeks, 25°C day and 18°C night (there was no heating in the fish-house during the summer), pH 7.4, 12°GH.

SPAWNING Spawning followed the usual 'T' formation. A total of 30 eggs were laid, approximately 2 mm in diameter. These were laid on the sides of the tank, on the box-filter and in the Java Moss. As with *C. hastatus* and *C. pygmaeus*, the eggs were laid singly.

FEEDING As for *C. acutus* (p. 39).

FRY Size at: 7 days – 3.5 mm; 1 month – 6.5 mm; 2 months – 10 mm. Adult coloration was reached in 6–7 weeks.

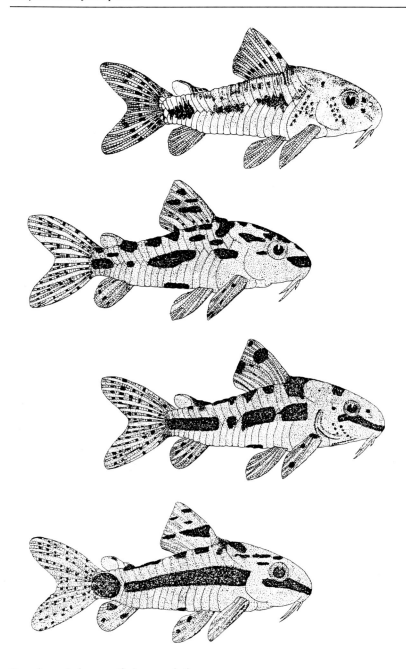

Corydoras habrosus. Colour variations.

Corydoras habrosus. Growth stages. From top to bottom: fry at 7 days; young fish at 4 weeks; young fish at 8 weeks.

Dainty Corydoras (*Corydoras habrosus*). Adult. Like *C. cochui*, this appears to be a pygmy species.

NOTE Considering the size of the female (30 mm), the size of the egg was large (2 mm). It was found that the fine sand caused considerable damage to the barbels of the fry (and many died), so this was replaced by 1.5 mm diameter gravel. The fine sand did not affect the adults at all.

Corydoras haraldschultzi
Knaak, 1962

Taxonomic Details
First collected by Harald Schultz.

ETYMOLOGY Named in honour of Harald Schultz.

Distribution
Brazil: Goiás – Rio Tocantins.

Description
C. haraldschultzi shares a similar colour pattern with *C. araguaiaensis* and *C. sterbai*. The pectoral and ventral fins are orange (as in *C. sterbai* but not *C. araguaianensis*). There are irregular black spots on the head (which are also found in *C. araguaiaensis*; in *C. sterbai* the spots are whitish) and 5–7 irregular vertical bars in the caudal fin (these are also present in *C. araguaiaensis*; *C. sterbai* has 4–8 bars).

SIZE The largest specimen examined was 52.5 mm, but this fish should grow to 60 mm in the aquarium.

Breeding
FISH USED 2 males, 35mm. 3 females, 38 mm. These were all wild-caught fish.

BREEDING-TANK 45 cm × 30 cm × 20 cm deep, furnished with a 1.5 cm layer of fine gravel, 1 box-filter and 1 nylon spawning-mop.

WATER Tap water that had been standing for 2 weeks; depth 15 cm, 24°C, pH 7.2, 8°GH.

SPAWNING *C. haraldschultzi* spawns following the typical *Corydoras* 'T' formation. A total of 23 eggs, measuring approximately 1.8 mm in diameter,

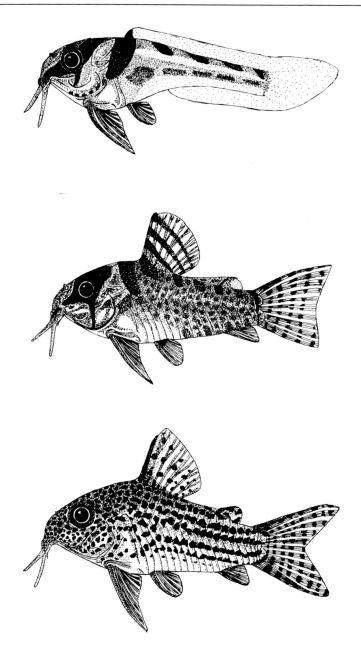

Corydoras haraldschultzi. Growth stages. From top to bottom: fry at 7 days; young fish at 4 weeks; young fish at 8–10 weeks.

were laid. Ten were deposited in the spawning-mop; the rest were placed on the side glass just above the gravel. The eggs were 100 per cent fertile and took 4–5 days to hatch. The fry were free-swimming 2 days later.

FEEDING The fry were fed as soon as they were free-swimming (when they had absorbed the yolk sac). They were given Microworms to begin with, followed by alternate feeds of pre-soaked powdered flake and small amounts of newly-hatched Brine Shrimps (live food one day, powdered food the next). As the fry grew, they were given Grindal Worms, sifted *Daphnia*, chopped *Tubifex*, White-worms and chopped Earthworms.

FRY Size at: 7 days – 5.5 mm; 1 month – 6.1 mm; 2 months – 6.75 mm.

NOTE These fish are slow methodical spawners. They will take a whole day to lay only a few eggs. No egg predation was observed.

Judging by the growth rate of the young, it was estimated that the fish used above were between 6 and 9 months old.

Corydoras hastatus
Eigenmann & Eigenmann, 1888
Dwarf Corydoras

Taxonomic Details
First collected in 1865/66 by Professor Louis Agassiz, a famous zoologist.

ETYMOLOGY From the Latin *hastatus* = 'spear-shaped'.

SYNONYMS *C. australe* Eigenmann & Ward, 1907

Distribution
Brazil: Amazonas – Villa Bella; Mato Grosso – Upper Rio Paraguai at Corumba. Paraguay: tributary of Rio Pilcomayo.

Description
C. hastatus is sometimes confused with *C. pygmaeus*, but lacks the dark band that runs through the centre of the body in *C. pygmaeus*. It merely exhibits a large blotch at the base of the caudal peduncle, which is sometimes margined in white.

Unlike most other *Corydoras*, which spend their time on the substrate, rummaging for food, *C. hastatus* spends most of its time swimming and eating in mid-water, usually in a shoal. In this respect, it is like *C. pygmaeus*. It seems happiest in a well-planted aquarium where it can sometimes be seen resting on the leaf of a plant. It is often imported with a small characin – possibly *Hemigrammus levis* – that shows the same colour pattern. It is caught with this fish in the wild where they seem to shoal together. This may be a form of protection based on the 'safety in numbers' theory.

SIZE The largest specimen examined was 19.7 mm, but in the aquarium the male should grow to 25 mm and the female to 30 mm.

Breeding
FISH USED 4 males, 20 mm. 2 females, 30 mm. These were all wild-caught fish.

BREEDING-TANK 25 cm × 20 cm × 20 cm deep, furnished with a 1.5 cm layer of well-washed river sand and 1 box-filter.

WATER Tap water that had been standing for 2 weeks; 23°C, pH 7.5, 14°GH.

SPAWNING The spawning usually followed the typical 'T' formation but, on some occasions, the mating took place in mid-water, as in *C. barbatus*.

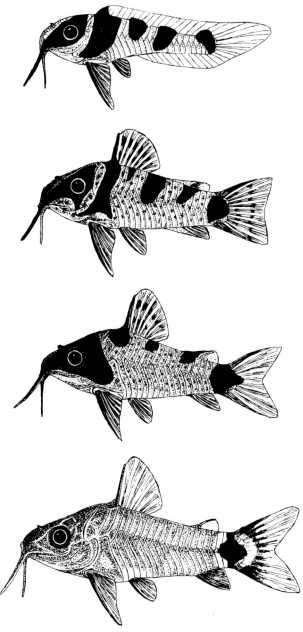

Corydoras hastatus. Growth stages. From top to bottom: fry at 7 days; young fish at 4 weeks; young fish at 6 weeks; young fish at 8 weeks.

Dwarf Corydoras (*Corydoras hastatus*). Adult. The male is smaller than the female.

Only 25 eggs were laid, measuring approximately 1 mm in diameter. These were all laid singly (as in *C. habrosus* and *C. pygmaeus*). After the eggs were laid, the adults were removed and placed in another tank for reconditioning. The water was then treated with methylene blue to eliminate any chance of fungal attack. The eggs all hatched on the fourth day and the fry were free-swimming 2 days later.

FEEDING   As for *C. acutus* (p. 39).

FRY   Size at: 7 days – 4 mm; 1 month – 8.5 mm; 2 months – 10.5 mm. Adult coloration was reached in 8–10 weeks.

NOTE   Live *Daphnia* seem to be essential for getting these fish into condition for breeding.

During pre-spawning activity, the eyes of the female dilate. When spawning is completed, their eyes return to normal. This is a good indication that they have finished and the adults can then be removed.

Corydoras heteromorphus
Nijssen, 1970

Taxonomic Details
First collected in 1967 by Dr Han Nijssen.

ETYMOLOGY   From the Latin *heteromorphus* = 'different form' or 'different shape'.

Distribution
Surinam: Saramacca – creek at right bank of Coppename River and Nickerie River system.

Description
SIZE   The largest specimen examined was 53 mm, but this species should grow to 55 mm in the aquarium.

Corydoras imitator
Nijssen & Isbrücker, 1983

Taxonomic Details
ETYMOLOGY From the Latin *imitator*, referring to the similarity in colour pattern to *C. adolfoi*.

Distribution
Brazil: Amazonas – Rio Negro.

Description
SIZE The largest specimen examined was 55.6 mm, but this species should grow to 60 mm in the aquarium.

Corydoras julii
Steindachner, 1906

Taxonomic Details
First collected in 1903 by F. Steindachner.

ETYMOLOGY Most probably named in honour of Mr Juli.

Distribution
Brazil: Maranno – creek into Rio Parnaiba.

Description
C. julii is similar to *C. leopardus*. Both species have a black blotch on the dorsal fin but the snout is shorter in *C. julii*.

SIZE The largest specimen examined was 38.3 mm, but this species should grow to 55 mm in the aquarium.

Corydoras lamberti
Nijssen & Isbrücker, 1986

Taxonomic Details
First collected in 1976 by C. Meyer.

ETYMOLOGY Named in honour of J. Lambert.

Distribution
Peru: Loreto – lower course of Rio Huytoyacu, right bank tributary of Rio Pastaza.

Description
SIZE The largest specimen examined was 38.4 mm, but this species should grow to 55 mm in the aquarium.

Corydoras latus
Pearson, 1924

Taxonomic Details
First collected in 1921 by N. E. Pearson.

ETYMOLOGY From the Latin *latus* = 'broad', alluding to the dimensions of this species.

Distribution
Bolivia: Beni – lagoons, Lago Rogoagua, Rio Beni basin.

Description
This is a deep-bodied, robust species which bears a superficial resemblance to *Brochis splendens*. The 2 species can be easily identified from an examination of the dorsal fin. In *B. splendens* this has a long base and 10–12 rays, whilst *C. latus* has a typical *Corydoras* short-based dorsal fin of 6–8 rays. Above the lateral line the body is dark, iridescent green, whilst below it is salmon-pink. When males are in good condition they develop a dark reticulated pattern throughout their body.

SIZE The largest specimen examined was 41.5 mm, but this species should grow to 75 mm in the aquarium.

Leopard Corydoras (*Corydoras leopardus*). Adult.

Corydoras leopardus
Myers, 1933
Leopard Corydoras

Taxonomic Details
Described from an aquarium specimen.

ETYMOLOGY   From the Latin *leopardus* = 'leopard-like', alluding to the colour pattern.

SYNONYMS   *C. funnelli* Fraser-Brunner, 1947

Distribution
Brazil: Pará – Rio Maracana, one of the coastal rivers south of the Amazon. Peru: Loreto – Rio Yavari, Cano, Buraco da Lucia and Cano de Guavariba near Lago Matamata. Ecuador: Napo – Quebrada to Rio Jutuncocha.

Description
C. leopardus has a similar colour pattern to *C. julii* and *C. trilineatus*, although it has a longer snout than either of these 2 species. All 3 species have a black blotch in the dorsal fin. The caudal fin of *C. leopardus* can have 5–7 irregular vertical bars (3–7 in *C. trilineatus*). The horizontal black line at the junction of the body scutes can vary in length: in some specimens of *C. leopardus* it reaches to below the dorsal fin whilst in others it extends nearly to the eye.

SIZE   The largest specimen examined was 49 mm, but this fish should grow to 65 mm in the aquarium.

Corydoras leucomelas
Eigenmann & Allen, 1942

Taxonomic Details
First collected in 1920 by W. R. Allen.

ETYMOLOGY   From the Latin *leucomelas* = 'with white and black'.

SYNONYMS   *C. caquetae* Fowler, 1943

Distribution

Ecuador: Napo – Rio Panayacu, tributary of Rio Napo, Jaton Cocha; Pastaza – Rio Pastaza. Colombia – Rio Orteguaze, Rio Florencia and Rio Caqueta. Peru: Ucayali – Rio Yarinacocha, a tributary of Rio Utiquinia; lagoon at Rio Utiquinia; Loreto, Maynas – Rio Nanay, Lorona Cocha, west of Iquitos, Rio Amazonas, 2–3 miles upstream from Leticia, Rio Chuinda into Lago Rimachi.

Description

C. leucomelas resembles *C. boehlkei*, but varies slightly in colour pattern. In some specimens of *C. leucomelas* all the dorsal fin is black except for the last ray; in others the black area is smaller and the pigment continues into the body. (In *C. boehlkei* the dark pigment is confined to the dorsal fin spine and first 2 rays – including the membrane – forming a wedge-shaped blotch.) The 2 soft rays are distinctly longer than the spine and, in some specimens, the spots on the body join together to form irregular lines (in *C. boehlkei* the spots are isolated). In some specimens again, the pigment over the eyes forms a bold black mask while in others it is very faint. (*C. boehlkei* lacks the pigment over the eyes altogether.) There are irregular, dark, vertical bars in the caudal fin and, in most specimens, an irregular black vertical bar at the base of the caudal fin. (Both of these are lacking in *C. boehlkei*.)

SIZE   The largest specimen examined was 41.3 mm, but this fish should grow to 55 mm in the aquarium.

Corydoras loretoensis
Nijssen & Isbrücker, 1986

Taxonomic Details

First collected in 1955 by M. Hohn (Catherwood Expedition to Peru).

ETYMOLOGY   Named after Loreto, the area where it was collected.

Distribution

Peru: Loreto, Maynas – Rio Nanay.

Corydoras leucomelas. Young adult.

Corydoras loretoensis. Young adult.

Description

C. loretoensis is reminiscent of *C. armatus* in colour pattern, but differs in a number of morphometric characters: body depth and width, length of dorsal and pectoral fin spines, snout length and depth of caudal peduncle. The body is covered with spots distributed in an irregular pattern. (In *C. armatus* the spots are smaller and lighter.) The dorsal fin spine has grey pigment, but the remainder of the dorsal and all other fins are hyaline. In most specimens examined there was a narrow, greyish, vertical line along the base of the caudal fin rays.

C. loretoensis and *C. armatus* occur sympatrically in some rivers.

[I took the above photograph of this fish about 12 years ago, and was only able to identify it after Nijssen & Isbrücker described it in 1986. I wonder why it took 31 years for this *Corydoras* to be named?]

SIZE   The largest specimen examined was 35.7 mm, but this fish should grow to 45 mm in the aquarium.

Corydoras loxozonus
Nijssen & Isbrücker, 1983

Taxonomic Details

First collected in 1969 by E. J. Hugghins.

ETYMOLOGY   From the Greek *loxos* = 'slanting' and the Latin *zona* = 'belt' or 'girdle', alluding to the dark oblique stripe on the body.

Distribution

Colombia: Meta – Lomalinda near Rio Ariari, tributary to Rio Guaviare.

Description

C. loxozonus has a similar colour pattern to *C. axelrodi*: both have a mask across the eye and a conspicuous dark oblique stripe on the body which occurs just below the dorsal fin in *C. loxozonus* and just above the junction of the body scutes of *C. axelrodi*. *C. loxozonus* has scattered pigment on the body, forming 3–5 irregular horizontal lines, and on the dorsal and

Corydoras loxozonus. Young adult.

caudal fins. (*C. axelrodi* has only 1 or 2 horizontal lines and no pigment in the dorsal and caudal fins.)

C. loxozonus is usually imported into the UK under the name of *C. 'deckeri'*.

SIZE The largest specimen examined was 35.7 mm, but this fish should grow to 55 mm in the aquarium.

Corydoras macropterus
Regan, 1913
High-fin Corydoras

Taxonomic Details
Described from an aquarium specimen.

ETYMOLOGY From the Latin *macropterus* = 'large wing', alluding to the fins.

SYNONYMS *C. bertoni* Eigenmann, 1942

Distribution
Brazil: Puerto Bertoni and Alto Paraná.

Description
C. macropterus is similar to *C. paleatus*, but differs in colour, being predominantly brown whereas *C. paleatus* is predominantly blue.

It is one of the species of *Corydoras* that exhibits sexual dimorphism: in adult males, the front of the pre-operculum is margined with bristles (these are absent in females). Males of only one other known species of *Corydoras* – *C. barbatus* – share this feature. The males of *C. macropterus* can also be distinguished from females by their longer pectoral fin spines and extended soft dorsal fin rays.

[The fish shown in the photograph on p. 86 was a present from a friend in 1975. He was a steward for an airline that flew regularly between the UK and the USA, where he purchased a pair of *C. macropterus*. Unfortunately, the female died before we had a chance of trying to breed them.]

SIZE The largest specimen examined was 51.5 mm. This fish should grow to 70 mm in the aquarium.

Corydoras maculifer
Nijssen & Isbrücker, 1971

Taxonomic Details
First collected by Dr R. H. Lowe-McConnell.

ETYMOLOGY From the Latin *maculifer* = 'carrying spots', alluding to the markings on this species.

Distribution
Brazil: Mato Grosso – Sangadina stream and Duaspontes stream, tributaries of the Rio Mortes.

Description
SIZE The largest specimen examined was 35 mm, but this species should grow to 65 mm in the aquarium.

Corydoras melanistius brevirostris
Fraser-Brunner, 1947

Taxonomic Details
Originally described from an aquarium specimen.

ETYMOLOGY From the Latin *brevis* = 'short', and *rostrum* = 'snout', alluding to the shorter snout of this subspecies.

SYNONYMS *C. wotroi*, Nijssen & Isbrücker, 1967

Distribution
Surinam: Brokopondo – Saramacca River system, Coratijn River system.

Description
C. m. brevirostris is often confused with *C. m. melanistius*, but the two can be separated quite easily by their different colour patterns and morphometric characters. In *C. m. brevirostris* the spots on the body are quite large (they are smaller and more numerous in *C. m. melanistius*) and the caudal fin has 4–7 intense, black, irregular vertical bars (it is clear in *C. m. melanistius*). *C. m. brevirostris* has a shorter head and a more robust body and, in some specimens, the blotch on the dorsal fin that continues into the body, and the mask, are less intense.

SIZE The largest specimen examined was 41.5 mm, but this fish should grow to 55 mm in the aquarium.

Breeding
C. m. brevirostris has been bred under aquarium conditions.

Corydoras melanistius melanistius
Regan, 1912
Black-spot Corydoras

Taxonomic Details
First collected by Mr Ehrhardt.

ETYMOLOGY From the Greek *melan* = 'black' and *histion* = 'sail', alluding to the dorsal fin.

Distribution
Guyana: Essequibo.

Description
C. m. melanistius is closely related to *C. bicolor* which lacks pigment spots on the head and body.

C. m. melanistius is often confused with *C. m. brevirostris*, but the 2 can be separated quite easily by their colour patterns and morphometric characters. In *C. m. melanistius* the spots on the body are small (they are larger and fewer in *C. m. brevirostris*), the caudal fin is clear (in *C. m. brevirostris* there are 4–7 intense, black, irregular, vertical bars), and the head is longer and the body less robust.

SIZE The largest specimen examined was 39.4 mm, but this fish should grow to 60 mm in the aquarium.

High-fin Corydoras (*Corydoras macropterus*). Young adult. When fully grown, males can be distinguished from females by their longer pectoral fin spines, extended dorsal fin rays and the bristles on the pre-operculum.

Corydoras melanistius brevirostris. Adult. The irregular black barring on the caudal fin distinguishes this subspecies from *C. m. melanistius*.

Breeding

SPAWNING   This usually follows after a cold-water-change has dropped the temperature to 16°C from 22°C. The fish breed in the typical 'T' formation.

Eggs are approximately 2 mm in diameter and are usually laid in Java Moss or in the corners of the tank. Eggs take 3–4 days to hatch.

FEEDING   As for *C. acutus* (p. 39).

FRY   Adult coloration is reached in 8–10 weeks.

Corydoras melanotaenia
Regan, 1912
Green/Gold Corydoras

Taxonomic Details
First collected in 1909 by B. Leighton.

ETYMOLOGY   From the Greek *melan* = 'black' and the Latin *taeniatus* = 'striped', alluding to the black band on the body.

Distribution
Colombia: Upper Rio Meta, Rio Manacacias, Rio Ocoa near Puerto Lopez, Rio Quenane and Rio Negro at Villavicencio.

Description
C. melanotaenia closely resembles some specimens of *C. aeneus* in colour pattern, but differs in a number of morphometric characters. The body is more slender and the snout length slightly longer and, when the fish is in good condition, the body and fins are a golden-yellow colour.

C. melanotaenia appears to be confined to Colombia, whereas *C. aeneus* has a widespread distribution. This is probably why there are so many colour variations of this species.

SIZE   The largest specimen examined was 47.8 mm, but this fish should grow to 70 mm in the aquarium.

Breeding
This species has been bred under aquarium conditions.

Corydoras melini
Lönnberg & Rendahl, 1930

Taxonomic Details
First collected in 1924 by Dr Douglas Melin.

ETYMOLOGY   Named in honour of Dr Douglas Melin.

Distribution
Brazil: Amazonas – Ivarete at confluence of Rio Papuri and Rio Uavpes, Rio Amazonas near Benjamin Constant. Ecuador: Pastaza – Rio Conambo, Rio Shione, Rio Pindo at confluence with Rio Tigre. Colombia: Rio Guaviare, Rio Vaupes and Rio Caqueta.

Description
C. melini has a similar colour pattern to *C. metae*. The dark body stripe divides into 2 just behind the dorsal fin and continues down into the lower half of the caudal peduncle and, in some specimens, into the lower lobe of the caudal fin. (In *C. metae* the dark body stripe runs along the ridge of the back and divides to run down each side of the caudal peduncle.) The dorsal fin in some specimens is entirely black, except for the tip. *C. melini* has a light-greyish ground colour (in *C. metae* the ground colour is tan, often with a pink hue) and is more slender in the body.

SIZE   The largest specimen examined was 46.6 mm, but the fish will probably only grow to about 45 mm in the aquarium.

Black-spot Corydoras (*Corydoras melanistius melanistius*). Adult. Note the clear caudal fin.

Green/gold Corydoras (*Corydoras melanotaenia*). Adult.

Corydoras melini. Adult. Adult coloration is reached in 10–12 weeks.

Breeding

SPAWNING These fish breed in the typical 'T' formation. The eggs, which are approximately 2.2 mm in diameter, are usually laid in Java Moss. (The eggs are not very adhesive and are easily damaged if you try to move them.) Eggs hatch in 4 days.

FEEDING As for *C. acutus* (p. 39).

FRY Adult coloration is reached in 10–12 weeks.

Corydoras metae
Eigenmann, 1914
Bandit Corydoras

Taxonomic Details
First collected in 1914 by M. Gonzales.

ETYMOLOGY Named after the Rio Meta, from which it was collected.

Distribution
Colombia: Rio Meta, Rio Guaviare, Rio Ocoa and Rio Manacacias.

Description
C. metae has a similar colour pattern to *C. melini*. A dark body stripe runs along the ridge of the back and divides to run down each side of the caudal peduncle. (In *C. melini* the dark body stripe divides into 2 just behind the dorsal fin and continues down into the lower half of the caudal peduncle; in some specimens it even continues into the lower lobe of the caudal fin.) The dorsal fin in some specimens is entirely black, except for the tip. The ground colour is tan, often with a pink hue (in *C. melini* it is light greyish) and the body is more robust.

SIZE The largest specimen examined was 42.8 mm, but this fish should grow to 50 mm in the aquarium.

Breeding
SPAWNING These fish breed in the typical 'T' formation. The eggs, which were laid singly, were approximately 2.25 mm in diameter and were deposited in Java Moss and on the sides of the tank. One female laid 30 eggs, but took a number of hours to do so. Eggs hatched in 4 days.

FEEDING As for *C. acutus* (p. 39).

FRY The fry grew quickly at first, but went through a very delicate stage at 5–6 weeks – approximately 20 per cent died. (This also happened in subsequent spawnings.) Adult coloration was reached in 8–10 weeks.

Bandit Corydoras (*Corydoras metae*). Adult. Adult coloration is reached in 8–10 weeks.

Corydoras micracanthus
Regan, 1912

Taxonomic Details
First collected by Mr Borelli.

Distribution
Argentina: Salta.

Description
SIZE   The largest specimen examined was 38.4 mm, but this species should grow to 50 mm in the aquarium.

Corydoras multimaculatus
Steindachner, 1907

Taxonomic Details
ETYMOLOGY   From the Latin *multi* = 'many', and *maculatus* = 'spotted', alluding to the many spots on the specimen.

Distribution
Brazil: Bahia – tributary of Rio Preto near Santa Rita de Cassia.

Description
SIZE   The largest specimen examined was 34.4 mm, but this species should grow to 65 mm in the aquarium.

Corydoras nanus
Nijssen & Isbrücker, 1967

Taxonomic Details
First collected in 1964 by Dr M. Boesman.

ETYMOLOGY   From the Latin *nanus* = 'dwarf'.

Distribution
Surinam: Brokopondo – Suriname River system, little tributaries of Gran Rio between Ligorio and Awaradam falls, Marowijne River system and little creek at right bank of Delmari River.

Description
C. nanus is similar to *C. elegans* and *C. napoensis*, apart from the differences in morphometric characters and colour pattern. It has ill-defined light areas on the body and a reticulated pattern in the dorsal fin which forms 3 irregular horizontal bands. (In *C. elegans* and *C. napoensis* the unpigmented areas on the body are more conspicuous and *C. napoensis* has a large oval blotch on the upper half of the dorsal fin.) The body of *C. nanus* is slimmer than that of *C. napoensis* and has 4 dark-brown to red-brown horizontal stripes, 1 below the lateral line and 3 above. It is a species in which the female grows larger than the male.

SIZE   The largest specimen examined was 44.7 mm, but males of this species should grow to 45 mm and females to 50 mm in the aquarium.

Breeding
FISH USED   3 males, 35 mm. 2 females, 45 mm.

BREEDING-TANK   20 cm × 20 cm × 20 cm deep, furnished with a 1.5 cm layer of fine gravel, 1 box-filter and a clump of Java Moss.

WATER   Tap water that had been standing for 2 weeks; depth 15 cm, 24°C, pH 6.8, 6°GH.

SPAWNING   The fish were placed in the breeding-tank. Some of the water was siphoned off and replaced with cold water which lowered the temperature of the tank from 24°C to 19°C.

Two days after the water-change the fish spawned in the typical *Corydoras* 'T' formation. The temperature of the water after spawning was 23°C. The eggs took 4 days to hatch and the fry were free-swimming 2 days later.

FEEDING As for *C. acutus* (p. 39).

FRY Size at: 7 days – 6 mm; 1 month – 11.5 mm. Adult coloration was reached at 3 months.

Corydoras nanus. Growth stages. From top to bottom: fry at 7 days; young fish at 4–6 weeks; young fish at 10–12 weeks.

Corydoras napoensis
Nijssen & Isbrücker, 1986

Taxonomic Details
First collected in 1954 by M. Ollala.

ETYMOLOGY Named after Napo, one of the regions from which it was collected.

Distribution
Ecuador: Napo – Rio Lagartococha, northern tributary to Rio Aguarico, Rio Napo drainage and Rio Jivino. Peru: Loreto – Rio Morona Cocha, Iquitos and Rio Nanay. Colombia: Rio Atacuari and Rio Amazonas.

Description
C. napoensis is similar to *C. elegans* and *C. nanus* but there are differences in morphometric characters as well as in colour pattern. In *C. napoensis* (and *C. elegans*) the unpigmented areas on the body are more conspicuous than the ill-defined light areas present in *C. nanus*. Adult males have a large black blotch in the dorsal fin (*C. elegans* and *C. nanus* have an irregular reticulated pattern). *C. napoensis* has a wide area of distribution and the colour pattern is different in both sexes. The colour of the male is more intense than the female. *C. napoensis* and *C. elegans* occur sympatrically in Ecuador and Peru.

SIZE The largest specimen examined was 42 mm, but this fish should grow to 50 mm in the aquarium.

Breeding
FISH USED 4 males, 35 mm. 2 females, 40 mm. These were all wild-caught fish.

BREEDING-TANK 45 cm × 20 cm × 15 cm deep, furnished with just 1 box-filter.

WATER Tap water that had been standing for 2 weeks; depth 10 cm, 23°C, pH 7.4, 12°GH.

SPAWNING Spawning followed the typical *Corydoras* 'T' formation. A total of 90 eggs were laid, measuring

Corydoras napoensis. Young adult. Colour patterns differ according to sex and the male is more intensely coloured.

approximately 1.5 mm in diameter. They were laid all over the tank in clutches of 3–6 at a time. The eggs were 95 per cent fertile. They hatched out in 4 days and fry were free-swimming 2 days later.

FEEDING As for *C. acutus* (p. 39).

FRY Size at: 7 days – 4.5 mm; 1 month – 7 mm; 2 months – 12.5 mm; 3 months – 18.5 mm. Adult coloration was reached after 10 weeks.

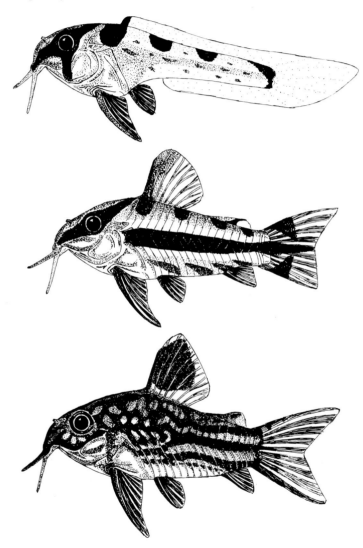

Corydoras napoensis. Growth stages. From top to bottom: fry at 7 days; young fish at 4 weeks; young fish at 8–10 weeks.

Corydoras narcissus
Nijssen & Isbrücker, 1980

Taxonomic Details
First collected in 1976 by H. R.
Axelrod.

ETYMOLOGY Named after Narcissus,
son of the Greek river god, Kephise.

Distribution
Brazil: Amazonas – Rio Purus system,
creek into Rio Ipixuna.

Description
This species is compared with *C.
arcuatus* on p. 46.

SIZE The largest specimen examined
was 64.7 mm, but this species should
grow to 65 mm in the aquarium.

Corydoras nattereri
Steindachner, 1877
Blue Corydoras

Taxonomic Details
First collected in 1865 by the Thayer
Expedition.

ETYMOLOGY Named in honour of
Johann Natterer, an Austrian collector.

Distribution
Brazil: Rio de Janeiro, affluent of Rio
Paranhyba; São Paulo – Rio Juquia;
Esperito Santo – Rio Doce Rio
Cambau, Rio Barra Seca.

Description
C. nattereri closely resembles *C.
prionotos* in colour pattern but it has a
shorter and more rounded snout and a
deeper body. The principle difference
between the 2 species is the absence in
C. nattereri, and the presence in *C.
prionotos*, of strongly-serrated pectoral
fin spines.

SIZE The largest specimen examined
was 51.6 mm, but this species should
grow to 65 mm in the aquarium.

Breeding
FISH USED 2 males, 45 mm. 1 female,
50 mm. These were all wild-caught
fish.

BREEDING-TANK 45 cm × 30 cm × 30
cm deep, furnished with a 1.5 cm layer
of fine gravel, 1 box-filter and 2
floating nylon spawning-mops.

WATER Tap water that had been
standing for 2 weeks; depth 20 cm,
22°C, pH 7.6, 14°GH.

SPAWNING The fish were placed in
the breeding-tank and were given a 30
per cent water-change (the tank being
topped up with cold water). The fish
spawned 2 days later, all 3 fish taking
part in the typical *Corydoras* 'T' formation. They produced 250 eggs which
were approximately 1.75 mm in diameter. 90 per cent of the eggs were
laid in the spawning-mops; the rest
were laid high on the sides of the tank.
75 per cent of the eggs were fertile and
took 4 days to hatch. The fry were
free-swimming after 2 days.

FEEDING As for *C. acutus* (p. 39).

FRY Size at: 7 days – 3.5 mm; 1 month
– 14 mm; 2 months – 18 mm; 3 months
– 21 mm. The fry grow at a fairly
moderate rate and reach adult coloration in 8–9 weeks.

Corydoras nijsseni
Sands, 1989

Taxonomic Details
ETYMOLOGY Named in honour of Dr
Han Nijssen.

Distribution
Brazil: tributary of the Rio Negro.

Description
SIZE The largest specimen examined was 27 mm, but this species should grow to 50 mm in the aquarium.

Breeding
This fish is reported to have been bred under aquarium conditions.

Corydoras octocirrus
Nijssen, 1970

Taxonomic Details
First collected in 1966 by Dr Han Nijssen.

ETYMOLOGY From the Latin *octocirrus* = '8 filaments' or '8 barbels', alluding to the 8 barbels on this fish (3 pairs rictal and 1 pair mental).

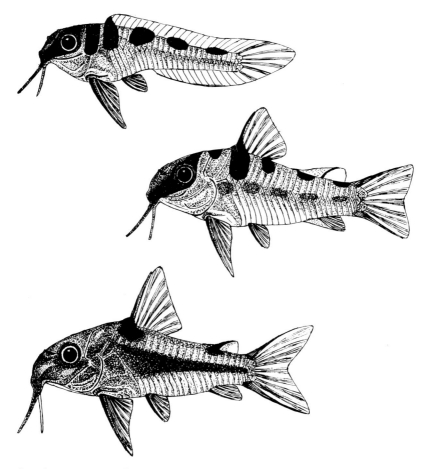

Corydoras nattereri. Growth stages. From top to bottom: fry at 7 days; young fish at 4 weeks; young fish at 8 weeks.

Distribution

Surinam: Brokopondo – Suriname River system, Marowijne River system and Marechai Creek.

Description

SIZE   The largest specimen examined was 65.7 mm, but this species should grow to 70 mm in the aquarium.

Corydoras oiapoquensis
Nijssen, 1972

Taxonomic Details

First collected in 1962 by J. P. Gosse.

ETYMOLOGY   Named after the Rio Oiapoque where the fish was collected.

Distribution

French Guiana: Inini – Cumuri creek at left bank of Oyapock River and Oyapock River system.

Description

SIZE   The largest specimen examined was 40.2 mm, but this species should grow to 55 mm in the aquarium.

Corydoras ornatus
Nijssen & Isbrücker, 1976

Taxonomic Details

First collected in 1974 by H. Baensch.

ETYMOLOGY   From the Latin *ornatus* = 'decorated'.

Distribution

Brazil: Rio Tapajos.

Description

C. ornatus shares the same colour pattern as *C. pulcher* Isbrücker &

Nijssen, 1973, *C. surinamensis* and *C. schwartzi*, but its body depth is the greatest. It has 3–4 longitudinal narrow stripes on the body; these are also present in the other 3 species but are broader in *C. pulcher*.

C. ornatus (and *C. pulcher*) lacks the dark pigment in the body which, in *C. schwartzi* and *C. surinamensis*, continues up into the dorsal fin. Black pigment is also present on the head of *C. ornatus* (and *C. pulcher*) but does not form the definite mask found in the other 2 species. The pigment in the caudal fin forms 5–7 irregular, vertical bars (4–6 in *C. pulcher* and 3–5 in *C. schwartzi* and *C. surinamensis*).

SIZE   The largest specimen examined was 54.2 mm, but this fish should grow to 65 mm in the aquarium.

Breeding

C. ornatus has been bred under aquarium conditions.

Corydoras orphnopterus
Weitzman & Nijssen, 1970

Taxonomic Details

ETYMOLOGY   From the Greek *orphnos* = 'dark' or 'dusky' and *pteron* = 'feather', 'wing' or 'fin', in reference to the black spot on the dorsal fin.

Distribution

Ecuador: Pastaza – lower Rio Bobonaza, Rio Pastaza system.

Description

SIZE   The largest specimen examined was 57.7 mm, but this species should grow to 65 mm in the aquarium.

Corydoras ornatus. Adult.

Corydoras osteocarus
Boehlke, 1951

Taxonomic Details
First collected in 1925 by C. Ternetz.

ETYMOLOGY From the Greek *osteon* = 'bone' and *kara* = 'head' or 'top'.

Distribution
Venezuela: San Fernando de Atabapo, where the Rio Atabapo (border river with Colombia) empties into the Orinoco River.

Description
C. osteocarus is similar to *C. sanchesi*, but differs in colour pattern. In *C. osteocarus* the dorsal fin spine, first soft ray and membrane are lightly spotted (in *C. sanchesi* they are dark grey). The first soft ray of the dorsal fin is never prolonged as it is in *C. sanchesi* and, in some males, the pigment on the junction of the body scutes joins up to form a thin horizontal line.
   C. osteocarus is another of the species where the males are a great deal more slender in the body than the females; the males are often mis-identified as *Aspidoras*.

SIZE The largest specimen examined was 35.1 mm, but this fish should grow to 45 mm in the aquarium.

Breeding
SPAWNING This usually takes place after a partial cold-water-change has reduced the temperature to 20°C from 24°C. Eggs of 1.5 mm diameter were laid singly. Eggs all hatched in 4 days.

FEEDING As for *C. acutus* (p. 39).

FRY Adult coloration is reached in 8–10 weeks.

Corydoras ourastigma
Nijssen, 1972

Taxonomic Details
First collected in 1967 by J. P. Gosse.

Distribution
Brazil: Acre – Rio Iquito, Rio Purus system.

Description

SIZE   The largest specimen examined was 60.1 mm, but this species should grow to 65 mm in the aquarium.

Corydoras oxyrhynchus
Nijssen & Isbrücker, 1967

Taxonomic Details
First collected in 1964 by M. Boesman.

ETYMOLOGY   From the Greek *oxys* = 'sharp' or 'acute' and *rhynchos* = 'snout', alluding to the long snout.

Distribution
Surinam: Brokopondo – Gojo Creek, a tributary of the Saramacca River.

Description
SIZE   The largest specimen examined was 50.8 mm, but this species should grow to 70 mm in the aquarium.

Corydoras paleatus
Jenyns, 1842
Peppered Corydoras

Taxonomic Details
First discovered by Charles Darwin on his epic voyage of the *Beagle*.

ETYMOLOGY   From the Latin *paleatus* = 'with dappled markings'.

SYNONYMS
Callichthys paleatus Jenyns, 1842
Corydoras maculatus Steindachner, 1879a
C. marmoratus Steindachner, 1879b
C. punctatus var. *argentina* Steindachner, 1879b
C. microcephalus Regan, 1912

Distribution
Argentina: Buenos Aires – small lake near Buenos Aires and Rio Paraná at San Pedro. Brazil: no exact location given. Uruguay: Montevideo.

Description
C. paleatus is sometimes confused with *C. ehrhardti*, but has a different colour pattern and body shape. The body depth is much greater and there are 3 blotches on the body (2 in *C. ehrhardti*). The remaining parts of the body and head (except for the ventral region) have irregularly scattered heavy pigment. (In *C. ehrhardti* the remaining parts of the body, except for the head, which is dark, and the ventral region, are lightly pigmented.) All the fins are heavily pigmented. (The fins of *C. ehrhardti* are usually without pigment – but if pigment is present it is barely visible.)

Most *C. paleatus* we see in the shops today are commercially bred in Singapore or Florida and they have lost the elongated finnage and some of the intense colour of the wild-caught specimens. The female of *C. paleatus* grows larger than the male. There is also an Albino strain.

[The fish shown opposite is a wild-caught specimen. It was purchased in the USA in 1975 and was given to my wife as a present.]

SIZE   The largest specimen examined was 51.1 mm, but the male of this species should grow to 65 mm in the aquarium and the female to 75 mm.

Breeding
SPAWNING   The habits of this fish are probably the most written about of all *Corydoras*. They spawn in the typical 'T' formation.

They lay eggs of approximately 1.75 mm diameter, usually on a corner-filter. Eggs hatch after 4 days.

FEEDING   As for *C. acutus* (p. 39).

FRY   Adult coloration is reached in 8–10 weeks.

Corydoras osteocarus. Adult. Males are more slender than females.

Peppered Corydoras (*Corydoras paleatus*). Adult male. Wild-caught specimen.

Corydoras panda
Nijssen & Isbrücker, 1971

Taxonomic Details
First collected in 1968 by R. H. Richards.

ETYMOLOGY 'Panda' alludes to the colour pattern of the fish.

Distribution
Peru: Huanuco – Rio Aquas, Rio Amarillas, tributary of Rio Pachitea, Rio Ucayali system.

Description
The basic body coloration is off-white, with a faint iridescent green sheen on the flanks and operculum. A black band circles the caudal peduncle between the adipose fin and caudal fin; this is widest at the lateral line. All fins are off-white except the dorsal fin, which is black becoming clear towards the outer margin, and the adipose fin, which has some black pigment. A black mask runs from the top of the head through the eyes; when viewed head-on, this gives the appearance of black eyes similar to a panda.

SIZE The largest specimen examined was 41.9 mm, but this species should grow to 55 mm in the aquarium.

Breeding
This species has been bred under aquarium conditions.

Corydoras pastazensis
Weitzman, 1963

Taxonomic Details
First collected in 1954 by R. Ollala.

ETYMOLOGY Named after Pastaza, the area where it was collected.

SYNONYMS *C. pastazensis orcesi* Weitzman & Nijssen, 1970

Distribution
Ecuador: Pastaza – Rio Pastaza, Rio Bobonaza, Rio Conambo, Rio Pindo, Rio Tigre system; Napo – Rio Napo drainage, Rio Jivino. Peru: Loreto – Rio Ucayali system.

Description
C. pastazensis varies in colour pattern depending on which river system it was collected from. A dark vertical bar (sometimes indistinct) occurs below the dorsal fin in all specimens; in some it continues up into the dorsal fin spine, first soft ray and membrane, finishing at the top. Some specimens have pigment on the head which forms a mask. The spotted pigment on the body in some specimens joins together to form irregular blotches. The caudal fin can have 4–9 narrow, irregular, vertical bars.

SIZE The largest specimen examined was 64 mm, but this fish should grow to 70 mm in the aquarium.

Corydoras polystictus
Regan, 1912

Taxonomic Details
First collected by C. Ternetz.

ETYMOLOGY From the Greek *poly* = 'many' and *stiktos* = 'spotted', alluding to the small spots on this species.

SYNONYMS *C. viriscens* A. de Miranda Ribeiro, 1912.

Distribution
Brazil: Mato Grosso – Doscalvides, Rio Paraguai at Caceres.

Corydoras pastazensis. Young adult. Specimens show a variation in colour pattern according to where they were collected.

Description

SIZE   The largest specimen examined was 29.4 mm, but this species should grow to 50 mm in the aquarium.

Corydoras potaroensis
Myers, 1927

Taxonomic Details
First collected in 1908 by C. H. Eigenmann and E. S. Shideler.

ETYMOLOGY   Named after the Potaro River, the location where the fish was collected.

Distribution
Guyana: Essequibo – Potaro River, creek below Potaro landing.

Description
SIZE   The largest specimen examined was 37.9 mm, but this species should grow to 55 mm in the aquarium.

Corydoras prionotos
Nijssen & Isbrücker, 1980

Taxonomic Details
First collected in 1963 by L. Travasses.

ETYMOLOGY   From the Greek *prionotos* = 'jagged' or 'serrated', alluding to the medial border of the pectoral fin spine.

Distribution
Brazil: Esperito Santo – Rio Doce system, Rio Cachimbau, Rio Jundia, Rio Cupido, Rio Cambau, Rio Barra Seca, Rio Juquia, Rio Daues, Rio de Janeiro.

Description
C. prionotos closely resembles *C. nattereri*, both species having similar colour patterns. *C. prionotos* has a more acute and longer snout and a more slender body shape than *C. nattereri*. The principal difference

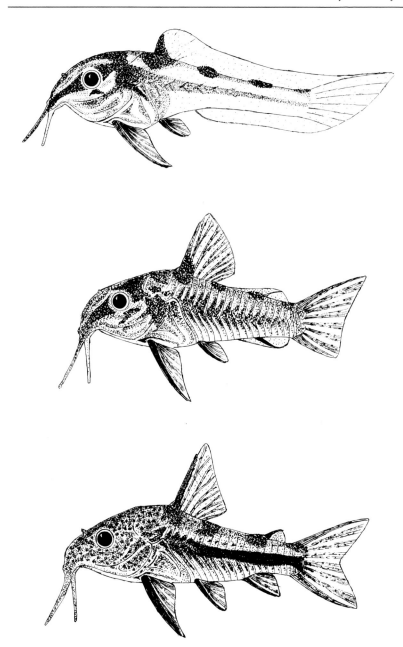

Corydoras prionotos. Growth stages. From top to bottom: fry at 7 days; young fish at 4–6 weeks; young fish at 10–12 weeks.

between the 2 species is the presence of strongly-serrated pectoral fin spines in *C. prionotos* (which are absent in *C. nattereri*).

SIZE   The largest specimen examined was 53.1 mm, but this species should grow to 65 mm in the aquarium.

Breeding
FISH USED   4 males, 40 mm. 1 female, 50 mm. These were all wild-caught fish.

BREEDING-TANK   45 cm × 20 cm × 15 cm deep, furnished with a 1 cm layer of very fine gravel, 1 box-filter and a small portion of Java Moss.

WATER   Tap water that had been standing for 2 weeks; depth 10 cm, 24°C, pH 6.8, 10°GH.

SPAWNING   The fish were placed in the tank and spawning took place without any inducement (no cold-water-change), and followed the typical *Corydoras* 'T' formation. A total of 50 eggs were laid, approximately 1.6 mm in diameter. They were placed equally on the tank sides and in the Java Moss. The adult fish were removed after spawning. The eggs took 4 days to hatch and the fry were free-swimming after a further 2 days.

FEEDING   As for *C. acutus* (p. 39).

FRY   Size at: 7 days – 6 mm; 1 month – 10.5 mm; 2 months – 18 mm; 3 months – 27 mm. Adult coloration was reached in 10–12 weeks.

NOTE   The normal procedure with smaller tanks was to change one-third of the water every week for cold, fresh water. In this case, there had not been a water change for 2 weeks. The adult fish had been fed every day with a range of live food including Brine Shrimps, Grindal Worms, *Daphnia*, Whiteworms and small amounts of *Tubifex* worms.

Corydoras pulcher
Isbrücker & Nijssen, 1973

Taxonomic Details
First collected in 1967 by W. Schwartz.

ETYMOLOGY   From the Latin *pulcher* = 'beautiful', alluding to the attractive colour pattern.

Distribution
Brazil: Rio Purus and Rio Amazonas system.

Description
C. pulcher appears to be most closely related to *C. schwartzi*. *C. pulcher* has 3–4 longitudinal, broad, dark stripes on the body (these stripes are narrow in *C. schwartzi*). The mid-lateral stripe is usually solid, but the others are somewhat irregular; the dorsal fin spine and first soft ray and membrane are yellowish and the caudal fin has 4–6 irregular, dark, vertical bars, sometimes broader in the lower lobe than in the upper.

C. pulcher and *C. schwartzi* occur sympatrically in the Rio Purus.

SIZE   The largest specimen examined was 41.2 mm, but this fish should grow to 55 mm in the aquarium.

Corydoras punctatus
(Bloch, 1794)
Spotted Corydoras

Taxonomic Details
First collected by M. E. Bloch.

ETYMOLOGY   From the Latin *punctatus* = 'spotted'.

Distribution
Surinam: Brokopondo – Suriname River system, Copagnie creek.

Corydoras pulcher. Adult.

Description
SIZE   The largest specimen examined was 41.8 mm, but this species should grow to 55 mm in the aquarium.

Corydoras pygmaeus
Knaack, 1966
Pygmy Catfish

Taxonomic Details
First collected by A. Smith.

ETYMOLOGY   From the Latin *pygmaeus* = 'dwarf', alluding to its small size.

Distribution
Ecuador: Napo – Rio Lagartococha, a northern tributary of Rio Aguarico. Peru: Loreto – Morona Cocha, west of Iquitos and Rio Nanay. Brazil: Rio Madeira near the mouth of Rio Jipirana.

Description
C. pygmaeus is easily distinguished from other species of *Corydoras* by its small adult size. It is sometimes confused with *C. hastatus*, but differs in its colour pattern. *C. pygmaeus* has a black band that runs through the centre of the body and broadens out into a blotch in the caudal peduncle. (*C. hastatus* does not exhibit the black band in the body and has a black blotch at the base of the caudal peduncle, which sometimes has a white margin.)

C. pygmaeus likes to swim in a shoal and is one of the few *Corydoras* species that likes to swim in mid-water. It seems to be happiest in a well-planted aquarium.

SIZE   The largest specimen examined was 23.7 mm, in the aquarium the male should grow to 25 mm and the female to 30 mm.

Breeding
SPAWNING   Usually no temperature reduction is needed to induce spawning. The fish spawn in the typical 'T' formation.

The eyes of the female dilate when spawning and return to normal after spawning is completed. Eggs of 1.75 mm diameter were laid singly and hatched in 3–4 days.

FEEDING   As for *C. acutus* (p. 39).

FRY   Adult coloration is reached in 6 weeks, and the fish can be breeding by 4 months.

Pygmy Catfish (*Corydoras pygmaeus*). Adult. Females are larger than males and adult coloration is reached in 6 weeks.

Corydoras rabauti
La Monte, 1941

Taxonomic Details
First collected in 1940 by A. Rabaut.

ETYMOLOGY   Named in honour of A. Rabaut.

SYNONYMS   *C. myersi* P. de Miranda Ribeiro, 1942

Distribution
Brazil: Amazonas – Rio Javari (border river between Brazil and Peru. Colombia: Rio Amacayacu tributary of the Rio Amazonas. Peru: Loreto – Rio Yavari, Rio Ucayali drainage, forest creeks at left bank of Rio Carahuayte.

Description
C. rabauti and *C. zygatus* share the same colour pattern when adult but the juveniles are completely different. The body stripe is slightly broader and darker (and in *C. zygatus* is bordered below with a green/gold sheen). In some specimens, a faint dark blotch across the eyes is visible (this is absent in *C. zygatus*). *C. rabauti* does not grow as large as *C. zygatus*.

C. rabauti was described by La Monte in 1941 from a juvenile fish which was 13.7 mm SL. *C. myersi* was described by P. de Miranda Ribeiro in 1942 from a fish that must have developed its adult coloration. One can see from the photographs on page 107 why there was confusion.

SIZE   The largest specimen examined was 48.8 mm, but this fish should grow to 55 mm in the aquarium.

Breeding
FISH USED   2 males, 38 mm. 2 females, 45 mm. These were all wild-caught fish.

BREEDING-TANK   25 cm × 20 cm × 20 cm deep, furnished with a 1.5 cm layer of fine, well-washed river sand, 1 box-filter, 2 nylon spawning-mops and a small portion of Java Moss.

WATER   Tap water that had been standing for 2 weeks; depth 15 cm, 22°C, pH 7.6, 14°GH.

SPAWNING   Spawning took place 2 days after a 20 per cent cold-water-change, which took the temperature down to

19°C. At the time of spawning, the temperature had risen again to 22°C. Spawning was in the typical 'T' formation. A total of 100 eggs were laid, each measuring approximately 1.75 mm in diameter. The eggs were deposited on the sides of the tank, in the Java Moss and in the nylon spawning-mops. They were all laid in small clusters of 3–6 at a time. The eggs took 4 days to hatch and the fry were free-swimming 2 days later.

FEEDING   As for *C. acutus* (p. 41).

FRY   Size at: 7 days – 4.5 mm; 2 weeks – 6 mm; 1 month – 8.5 mm; 6 weeks – 10 mm; 2 months – 15 mm.

NOTE   The colour pattern of the fry of *C. rabauti* is completely different to that of the fry of the similarly-coloured adult *C. zygatus*. *C. rabauti* fry are very striking at 4 weeks old (see below) and they reach adult coloration in 8–10 weeks.

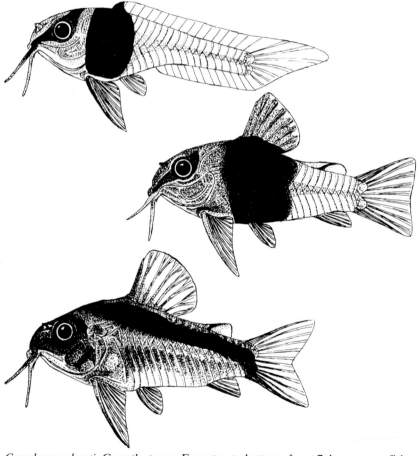

Corydoras rabauti. Growth stages. From top to bottom: fry at 7 days; young fish at 4–6 weeks; young fish at 10–12 weeks.

Corydoras rabauti. Adult.

Corydoras rabauti. Juvenile. Note that this fish has not yet formed its finnage.

Mosaic Corydoras (*Corydoras reticulatus*). Young adult.

Corydoras reticulatus
Fraser-Brunner, 1938
Mosaic Corydoras

Taxonomic Details
Described from an aquarium specimen, but some of the first specimens were collected in 1935 by W. G. Scherer.

ETYMOLOGY   From the Latin *reticulata* = 'with a reticulated pattern' or 'net-like design'.

Distribution
Brazil: Rio Amazonas at Monte Alegre. Peru: Loreto – Rio Ampiyacu, Rio Nanay.

Description
C. reticulatus shares the same colour pattern with *C. bolivianus* and *C. sodalis*. *C. reticulatus* and *C. sodalis* are extremely variable in colour pattern; the body can be covered with small irregular dots and spots *or* large spots and blotches which link up to form a reticulated pattern – there is also a great variation in the reticulated pattern. The caudal fins can have 4–8 irregular vertical bars. In *C. reticulatus* the dorsal fin has irregular pigment and a black blotch (some specimens lack the irregular pigment, but the black blotch is always present). (*C. sodalis* has scattered pigment in the dorsal fin and in some specimens this joins together to form 1 or 2 horizontal stripes.)

SIZE   The largest specimen examined was 30.7 mm, but this fish should grow to 65 mm in the aquarium.

Breeding
C. reticulatus has been bred under aquarium conditions.

Corydoras revelatus
Cockerell, 1925

Tertiary fossil found in Argentina.

Corydoras reynoldsi
Myers and Weitzman, 1960

Taxonomic Details
First collected in 1958 by G. S. Myers, T. D. White, J. N. Reynolds and L. Wulff.

ETYMOLOGY   Named in honour of J. N. Reynolds.

Distribution
Colombia: Caquera – small tributary of Rio Orreguaza and Rio Caquera system.

Description
SIZE   The largest specimen examined was 31.4 mm, but this species should grow to 35 mm in the aquarium.

Corydoras robineae
Burgess, 1983
Flag-tailed Corydoras

Taxonomic Details
First collected by Adolfo Schwartz.

ETYMOLOGY   Named in honour of Robine Schwartz.

Distribution
Brazil: Amazonas – Rio Aiuana tributary of Rio Negro.

Description
SIZE·   The largest specimen examined was 43.9 mm, but this species should grow to 60 mm in the aquarium.

Corydoras robustus
Nijssen & Isbrücker, 1980

Taxonomic Details
First collected in 1976 by Dr H. R. Axelrod.

ETYMOLOGY From the Latin *robustus* = 'robust' or 'strong', in reference to the dimensions of the fish.

Distribution
Brazil: Amazonas – Rio Purus system, creek into Rio Ipixuna.

Description
SIZE The largest specimen examined was 71.2 mm, but this species should grow to 75 mm in the aquarium.

Corydoras sanchesi
Nijssen & Isbrücker, 1967

Taxonomic Details
First collected in 1964 by M. Boesman.

ETYMOLOGY Possibly named after Mr Sanches.

Distribution
Surinam: Brokopondo – Gojo Creek above Posoegroenoe, a tributary of the Saramacca River.

Description
C. sanchesi is similar to *C. osteocarus* but differs in colour pattern. Also, the dorsal fin spine, first soft ray and membrane are dark grey whereas they are lightly spotted in *C. osteocarus*. The first soft ray of the dorsal fin is prolonged (which never occurs in *C. osteocarus*).

SIZE The largest specimen examined was 41 mm, but this species should grow to 45 mm in the aquarium.

Corydoras saramaccensis
Nijssen, 1970

Taxonomic Details
First collected in 1967 by Dr Han Nijssen.

ETYMOLOGY Named after the Saramacca River, the location where the fish was collected.

Distribution
Surinam: Brokopondo – Saramacca River system.

Description
SIZE The largest specimen examined was 51.3 mm, but this fish should grow to 60 mm in the aquarium.

Corydoras schwartzi
Rossel, 1963

Taxonomic Details
First collected in 1962 by Adolfo Schwartz.

ETYMOLOGY Named in honour of Adolfo Schwartz.

Distribution
Brazil: Amazonas – mouth of Rio Purus.

Description
This species is compared with *C. ornatus* on p. 96.

SIZE The largest specimen examined was 34.5 mm, but this species should grow to 60 mm in the aquarium.

Corydoras semiaquilus
Weitzman, 1964

Taxonomic Details
First collected in 1960 by H. Schultz.

ETYMOLOGY From the Latin *semi* = 'half' and *aquilus* = 'dark-coloured', alluding to the dark colour on the upper body scutes.

Distribution
Peru: Loreto – Rio Ucayali system. Brazil: Amazonas – Rio Solimões.

Description
C. semiaquilus is similar in colour pattern to several other long-snouted species: *C. amapaensis*, *C. septentrionalis*, *C. solox* and *C. treitlii*. All these species exhibit a large blotch on the mid-side of the body. In *C. semiaquilus* the pigment covers most of the body, which makes it easy to distinguish from other *Corydoras*. (In *C. amapaensis* the blotch varies in size, intensity of colour and distribution. In *C. septentrionalis* it is confined to below the dorsal fin. In *C. solox* it is narrow and wedge-shaped, confined to the upper body scutes, starting below the dorsal fin spine and ending at the caudal peduncle. In *C. treitlii* it is wedge-shaped, starting behind the operculum and finishing at the caudal peduncle.) Of the 5 species mentioned, only *C. semiaquilus* and *C. septentrionalis* have pigment in the caudal fin.

C. semiaquilus inhabits small jungle rivers at the headwaters of the blackwater creeks which empty into the upper Rio Solimões. These small and narrow creeks have crystal-clear water and sandy bottoms covered with pebbles and rotting leaves.

SIZE The largest specimen examined was 60.9 mm, but this fish should grow to 70 mm in the aquarium.

Corydoras septentrionalis
Gosline, 1940

Taxonomic Details
First collected in 1939 by F. F. Bond.

ETYMOLOGY From the Latin *septentrionalis* = (northern), alluding to the fact that this fish comes from northern South America.

Distribution
Venezuela: Monagas – Rio Pina, Rio Guarapiche system, Rio Amana, Rio Guanipa system and Rio Tinaquillo.

Description
C. septentrionalis is very similar in colour pattern to several other long-snouted species: *C. amapaensis*, *C. semiaquilus*, *C. simulatus*, *C. solox* and *C. treitlii*. All these species, except *C. simulatus* (see below), exhibit the large blotch on the mid-side of the body. (In *C. septentrionalis* it is confined to below the dorsal fin. In *C. amapaensis* this blotch varies in size, intensity of colour and distribution. In *C. semiaquilus* it covers most of the body. In *C. solox* it is narrow and wedge-shaped, confined to the upper body scutes, and starting below the dorsal fin spine and ending at the caudal peduncle. In *C. treitlii* it is wedge-shaped, starting behind the operculum and finishing at the caudal peduncle.) Of these 6 species, only *C. septentrionalis*, *C. simulatus* and *C. semiaquilus* have pigment in the caudal fin.

C. septentrionalis has a feature that is known in only 2 other species of *Corydoras* (*C. amapaensis* and *C. octocirrus* Nijssen, 1970): it possesses 3 pairs of rictal barbels; only 2 pairs are found in all other known species.

SIZE The largest specimen examined was 48.1 mm, but this fish should grow to 65 mm in the aquarium.

Corydoras similis
Hieronimus, 1991

Taxonomic Details
ETYMOLOGY Named for its similarity to *C. ourastigma*.

Distribution
Brazil: Rio Madeira.

Description
SIZE The largest specimen examined was 37.5 mm, but this species should grow to 45 mm in the aquarium.

Corydoras simulatus
Weitzman & Nijssen, 1970

Taxonomic Details
ETYMOLOGY From the past particle of the Latin *simulare* = 'to imitate', in reference to the similarity of the colour pattern of this species to that of *C. metae*, also from the Rio Meta system and found with *C. simulatus*.

Distribution
Colombia: Rio Ocoa, Rio Meta system and Rio Manacacias.

Description
Although the colour pattern of *C. simulatus* superficially resembles that of the short-snouted *C. metae* they are not closely related. In fact, *C. simulatus* is closely related to the long-snouted *C. septentrionalis*.

Both have very similar colour patterns, but in each species a different part of the colour pattern is emphasised. *C. simulatus* has a large black blotch in the dorsal fin (which is absent in *C. septentrionalis*) and the pigment on the body, at the base of the dorsal fin, is very dark, forming a distinct blotch, whereas the pigment here is relatively weak and pale in *C. septentrionalis*.

Along the mid-side, from the ventral to the mid-dorsal fin spine, *C. simulatus* shows irregular pigmentation (in *C. septentrionalis* this area has a large, black body blotch) and the dorsal ends of the dorso-lateral scutes bear dark pigment (very pale in *C. septentrionalis*). Both species have dark pigment on the caudal peduncle.

The head of *C. simulatus* has a great deal of black pigment, forming a diffused black mask across the eye. In *C. septentrionalis* there is a similar distribution of pigment but it is much paler and does not form a mask.

Both species show 6–7 irregular vertical bars in the caudal fin.

C. simulatus has 2 pairs of rictal barbels and *C. septentrionalis* has 3 pairs – a feature that it shares with two other species of *Corydoras*.

SIZE The largest specimen examined was 54.6 mm, this fish should grow to 65 mm in the aquarium.

Corydoras sodalis
Nijssen & Isbrücker, 1986

Taxonomic Details
First collected in 1971 by T. Hongslo.

ETYMOLOGY From the Latin *sodalis* = 'the companion', alluding to the exterior resemblance to *C. reticulatus*.

Distribution
Peru: Loreto – Rio Yavari, Cano de Guavariba into Lago Matmata. Brazil: Amazonas – Costa de Capacete, Rio Solimões at Benjamin Constant.

Description
C. sodalis shares the same colour pattern as *C. reticulatus* (p. 108) and *C. bolivianus*.

Corydoras semiaquilus. Adult.

Corydoras septentrionalis. Young adult.

Corydoras simulatus. Young adult.

Corydoras sodalis. Adult.

This pattern is extremely variable. The upper half of the body may be covered with small irregular dots and spots, or large spots and blotches, which link up to form a reticulated pattern. (In *C. bolivianus* this pattern extends into the ventral region.) Scattered pigment in the dorsal fin sometimes forms 1 or 2 horizontal stripes. (In *C. reticulatus* there is scattered pigment and a dark blotch on the dorsal fin whereas, in *C. bolivianus*, all the fins are heavily pigmented and there is no blotch.) The caudal fin may be covered with small spots, forming up to 7 irregular vertical bars but, in some specimens, the pigment may form oblique bars in a chevron-like pattern. The dark line along the junction of the body scutes (when present) can be either straight or zigzag and, in some specimens, a broad unpigmented area is present above this line.

SIZE The largest specimen examined was 48.6 mm, but this fish should grow to 65 mm in the aquarium.

Breeding
C. sodalis has been known to have bred under aquarium conditions.

Corydoras solox
Nijssen & Isbrücker, 1983

Taxonomic Details
First collected in 1976 by F. d'Aubenton, G. Vidy and M. Filey.

ETYMOLOGY From the Latin *solox*, alluding to the bristles on the pectoral fin spines of the adult male.

Distribution
Brazil: Amapá – Rio Oiapoque.

Description
This species is compared with *C. septentrionalis* on p. 110.

SIZE The largest specimen examined was 62.5 mm, but this species should grow to 70 mm in the aquarium.

Corydoras spilurus
Norman, 1926
Striped Corydoras

Taxonomic Details
First collected in 1926 by C. Ternetz.

ETYMOLOGY From the Latin *spilurus* = 'with spots on the tail'.

Distribution
French Guiana: Inini – Iponcin creek into Approuage river.

Description
SIZE The largest specimen examined was 47.9 mm, but this species should grow to 55 mm in the aquarium.

Corydoras steindachneri
Isbrücker & Nijssen, 1973

Taxonomic Details
ETYMOLOGY Named in honour of Dr Franz Steindachner, the Austrian ichthyologist (1834–1919).

Distribution
Brazil: Paraná – Paranagua.

Description
SIZE The largest specimen examined was 40.4 mm, but this species should grow to 50 mm in the aquarium.

Breeding
It is reported to have been bred in the aquarium, but the fish figured with the reported spawning was not *C. steindachneri* but an undescribed species.

Corydoras stenocephalus
Eigenmann & Allen, 1942

Taxonomic Details
First collected in 1920 by W. R. Allen.

ETYMOLOGY From the Latin *stenocephalus* = 'narrow-headed'.

Distribution
Peru: Loreto – Rio Ampiyacu; Ucayali – Lake Yarinacocha, Rio Ucayali system, Quebrada Pyuayci, tributary to Pachitea, Rio Nashua; Madre de Dios – Rio Tombopata system and

Rio Madre de Dios. Ecuador: No exact locations are known.

Description
C. stenocephalus is sometimes confused with *C. acutus* (p. 39) whose body proportions are the same, but which displays a completely different colour pattern.
   C. stenocephalus varies considerably in its colour pattern. Some specimens have a pale-tan ground colour all over, others (especially those from Rio Madre de Dios) display a large, bold, triangular blotch on the body scutes, starting below the dorsal fin spine and ending below the adipose fin. Some specimens have 2 large blotches on the body scutes, one below the dorsal fin and a slender tapering one below the adipose fin. (In *C. acutus* the pigment on the body forms irregular spots and lines.) *C. stenocephalus* has no pigment in the dorsal and caudal fins but *C. acutus* has a blotch in the dorsal fin and 4–11 irregular vertical bars in the caudal fin.
   C. stenocephalus was thought to be a synonym of *C. acutus*, but it is now known to be a distinct species.

SIZE The largest specimen examined was 63.55 mm, but this fish should grow to 70 mm in the aquarium.

Breeding
This species has been bred under aquarium conditions.

Corydoras sterbai
Knaack, 1962

Taxonomic Details
First collected by H. Schultz.

ETYMOLOGY Named in honour of Gunther Sterba.

Distribution
Brazil: No exact location given.

Description
C. sterbai has a similar colour pattern to *C. haraldschultzi* and *C. araguaiensis*. Like *C. haraldschultzi*, the pectoral and ventral fins are orange (they are not in *C. araguaiensis*). There are irregular white spots on the head and 4–8 irregular bars on the caudal fin. (In the other two species the spots are black and there are 5–7 bars on the caudal fin).

SIZE The largest specimen examined was 56.4 mm, but this species should grow to 60 mm in the aquarium.

Corydoras surinamensis
Nyssen, 1970

Taxonomic Details
First collected in 1967 by Dr Han Nijssen.

ETYMOLOGY Named after Surinam, the country where the fish was collected.

Distribution
Surinam: Saramacca – creek at right bank of Coppename River.

Description
This species is compared with *C. ornatus* on p. 96.

SIZE The largest specimen examined was 42.3 mm, but this species should grow to 60 mm in the aquarium.

Corydoras sychri
Weitzman, 1961

Taxonomic Details
First collected in 1956/57.

ETYMOLOGY Named in honour of Al Sychr of Hayward, California, USA. who gave the original aquarium specimens to Dr Weitzman to describe. Al Sychr (pronounced Si-ker) is an aquarist with a special interest in the genus *Corydoras*, and has given Dr Weitzman many specimens to study.

Distribution
At first no exact location could be given for this fish as it was described from an aquarium specimen, but we now know that it is found in Peru in Prov. Maynas, Rio Nanay and Rio Amazonas near Iquitos.

Description
C. sychri has a similar colour pattern to *C. atropersonatus*, but in *C. sychri* the spots on the body are smaller and more numerous. The 2 species differ in a number of morphometric characters: body width, snout length and the number of lateral body scutes.

SIZE The largest specimen examined was 52 mm, but these fish usually grow to about 50 mm in the aquarium.

Breeding
SPAWNING These fish usually spawn in the typical 'T' formation. Eggs of approximately 1.5–1.7 mm in diameter were laid in Java Moss and on the sides of the tank. The adults were removed from the tank as soon as spawning was finished, otherwise they would have eaten all the eggs. The eggs took 3–4 days to hatch.

FEEDING As for *C. acutus* (p. 39).

FRY Adult coloration is reached in 7–8 weeks.

Corydoras stenocephalus. Young adult. The colour pattern shows considerable variation.

Corydoras sychri. Adult. Adult coloration is reached in 7–8 weeks.

Corydoras treitlii. Young adult.

Corydoras treitlii
Steindachner, 1906
Long-nosed Corydoras

Taxonomic Details
First collected in 1903 by F. Steindachner.

ETYMOLOGY   Named in honour of Mr Treitl.

Distribution
Brazil: Maranhão – creek into Rio Parnaiba.

Description
C. treitlii is possibly related to *C. fowleri* (p. 68), but differs in a number of morphometric characters and colour pattern. It has fine bony prickles on the thoracic and abdominal plates (in *C. fowleri* they are imbricated) and a shorter body in relation to head length. It is also very similar in colour pattern to several other long-snouted species: *C. amapaensis*, *C. semiaquilus*, *C. septentrionalis* and *C. solox* (see p. 112 for a comparison). All these species exhibit a large blotch on the mid-side of the body; this is wedge-shaped in *C. treitlii* and starts behind the operculum and finishes at the caudal peduncle. (In *C. amapaensis* this blotch varies in size, intensity of colour and distribution; in *C. semiaquilus* it covers most of the body; in *C. septentrionalis* it is confined to below the dorsal fin; in *C. solox* it is narrow and wedge-shaped, confined to the upper body scutes, starting below the dorsal fin spine and ending at the caudal peduncle.)

SIZE   The largest specimen examined was 52.5 mm, but this fish should grow to 70 mm in the aquarium.

Breeding
SPAWNING   This took place in typical 'T' formation after a 25 per cent cold-water-change which reduced the temperature to 20°C from 24°C. The eggs laid were 1–1.5 mm in diameter and they were deposited in the Java Moss. The eggs hatched in 3–4 days.

FEEDING   As for *C. acutus* (p. 39).

FRY   Young reached adult coloration in 9–10 weeks. Their growth started off at a steady rate until approximately 3 months and then slowed down.

Corydoras trilineatus
Cope, 1872
Three-lined Corydoras

Taxonomic Details
First collected by J. Hauxwell.

ETYMOLOGY   From the Latin *trilineatus*, referring to the presence of the 3 lateral bands.

SYNONYMS
C. episcopi Eigenmann & Allen, 1942
C. dubius Nijssen & Isbrücker, 1967

Distribution
Ecuador: Pastaza – Rio Capahuary, tributary of Rio Pastaza, Jatuncoha (lake) at Rio Yasuni, Rio Napo system, Rio Bobonaza at Chicherota; Napo – Rio Yasuni drainage, Quebrada to Rio Jatuncocha. Colombia: Rio Caqueta. Peru: Loreto – Rio Ampiyacu, Pebas Cano, Rio Morona, Yarina Cocha (lake), Rio Ucayali system, Rio Yavari, Rio Pastaza, Rio Huytoyacu, Rio Nanay drainage, west of Iquitos; Ucayali – tributary to Rio Utiquinia, lagoon at Rio Utiquinia.

Description
C. trilineatus has a similar colour pattern to *C. julii* and *C. leopardus*. *C. trilineatus* and *C. julii* have short snouts whilst *C. leopardus* has a longer

snout. *C. trilineatus* is extremely variable in colour pattern: the black blotch in the dorsal fin varies in size and intensity; the caudal fin can have from 3–7 irregular vertical bars (5–7 in *C. leopardus*); the head and body is covered with small irregular spots or blotches, and in some specimens they join up to form black vermiculated lines (in *C. julii* the head is spotted). In most specimens of *C. trilineatus*, a black, sometimes irregular, horizontal zigzag line is present at the junction of the body scutes, and this line is margined at either side by an unpigmented area. *C. trilineatus* has a more robust body than *C. julii*, which has a slender body.

SIZE The largest specimen examined was 44.9 mm, but this fish should grow to 55 mm in the aquarium.

Breeding

SPAWNING The temperature of the fish-house dropped during the day from 26°C to 19°C. The next day the fish spawned following the typical 'T' formation. Eggs of approximately 1.75 mm diameter were deposited in all corners of the tank. The eggs hatched in 3–4 days.

FEEDING As for *C. acutus* (p. 39).

FRY Adult coloration was reached in 10–12 weeks.

Corydoras undulatus
Regan, 1912

Taxonomic Details
ETYMOLOGY From the Latin *undulatus* = 'wavy'.

Distribution
Argentina: Buenos Aires, La Plata. Brazil: No exact location known. Paraguay: No exact location known.

Description
C. undulatus is one of the most confusing species where colour pattern is concerned. Both sexes display a variety of different colour patterns. The colour of some male specimens tends to be more intense while, in others, the body is scattered with spots and flecks which form irregular horizontal lines. In some specimens of both sexes the body is covered with pigment, which forms irregular blotches, and the paler ground colour of the body forms an irregular reticulated pattern (similar to the pattern formed in the dark pigment on the body in some specimens of *C. reticulatus* and *C. sodalis*). In some specimens all the fins are irregularly pigmented, sometimes heavily. Even if the dorsal fin is heavily pigmented, *C. undulatus* never shows the dark black blotch that is present in some adult males of *C. napoensis*. Just to add to the confusion, males and females share the same body shape.

C. undulatus was first imported into the UK in 1909 by J. P. Arnold.

SIZE The largest specimen examined was 43.9 mm, but this fish should grow to 55 mm in the aquarium.

Breeding
SPAWNING This took place in typical 'T' formation after a cold-water-change which took the temperature down to 17°C from 22°C. Six males and 4 females were used and spawning was frenzied. Over 700 eggs were laid, 1.5 mm in diameter. 80 per cent proved to be fertile and hatched in 4 days.

FEEDING As for *C. acutus* (p. 39).

FRY Adult coloration was reached in 8–10 weeks.

Three-lined Corydoras (*Corydoras trilineatus*). Adult. Adult coloration is reached in 10–12 weeks.

Corydoras undulatus. Young male. Both sexes display a variety of different colour patterns.

Corydoras zygatus. Adult. This species has the same colour pattern as *C. rabauti* when adult although the juveniles are completely different.

Corydoras weitzmani
Nijssen, 1971

Taxonomic Details
First collected in 1949 by C. Kalinowski.

ETYMOLOGY Named in honour of S. H. Weitzman.

Distribution
Peru: Cuzco – Rio Vilcanota system at Cuzco.

Description
SIZE The largest specimen examined was 46.7 mm, but this species should grow to 55 mm in the aquarium.

Corydoras xinguensis
Nijssen, 1972

Taxonomic Details
First collected in 1964 by J. P. Gosse.

ETYMOLOGY Named after the Xingu River in Brazil, where this fish was found.

Distribution
Brazil: Mato Grosso – Suia Missu creek, tributary of the upper Rio Xingu, Rio Ampari system.

Description
SIZE The largest specimen examined was 43.2 mm, but this species should grow to 50 mm in the aquarium.

Corydoras zygatus
Eigenmann & Allen, 1942

Taxonomic Details
First collected in 1920 by W. R. Allen.

ETYMOLOGY From the Greek *zygados* = 'team' or 'pair', possibly alluding to the close resemblance to *C. rabauti*.

Distribution
Peru: Loreto – Rio Huallaga system, Yurimaguas; Rio Amazonas – Rio Santiago near Caterpiza. Ecuador: Pastaza – Lower Rio Bobonaza, tributary to Rio Pastaza, mouth of Rio Pindo, a tributary to Rio Tigre.

Description
C. zygatus and *C. rabauti* are very similar as adults. However, the juveniles of each species are completely different (see opposite). Once adult coloration is reached at about 8–10 weeks of age, *C. zygatus* has a dark body stripe that is faded in an area just below the adipose fin. This body stripe only extends as far as the caudal peduncle. (In *C. rabauti* the body stripe, which is broader and darker, extends across the caudal peduncle and sometimes into the rays of the lower lobes of the caudal fin.)

In *C. zygatus* the body stripe is bordered below by a green/gold sheen which is absent in *C. rabauti*.

C. zygatus does not have the dark pigment across the eyes that some specimens of *C. rabauti* display and it also grows larger than *C. rabauti*.

SIZE The largest specimen examined was 55.5 mm, but this fish should grow to 70 mm in the aquarium.

Breeding
FISH USED 4 males, 40 mm. 2 females, 55 mm. These were all wild-caught fish.

BREEDING-TANK 45 cm × 45 cm × 30 cm deep, furnished with a 2 cm layer of gravel (4 mm diameter) and 1 box-filter.

WATER Tap water that had been standing for 2 weeks; depth 20 cm, 22°C, pH 7.2, 14°GH.

Corydoras zygatus. Growth stages. From top to bottom: fry at 7 days; young fish at 4–6 weeks; young fish at 10–12 weeks.

SPAWNING 60 per cent of the water was changed for fresh cold water; this reduced the temperature to 16°C. The fish spawned within hours of the water-change in the typical 'T' formation.

A total of 1,200 eggs were laid by the 2 females and measured approximately 1 mm in diameter. The eggs were deposited within the top 7.5 cm of water; a few were even laid out of the water, such was the enthusiasm of the females. Considering the large number of eggs, very few were infertile (3 per cent). The fry started to emerge after 3 days and all the eggs hatched by the end of the fourth day. 2 days later they were all free-swimming.

FEEDING As soon as the fry were free-swimming they were given their first feed of Microworms. This was supplemented on alternate feeds with pre-soaked flake and newly-hatched Brine Shrimps. The fry grew rapidly and were soon taking larger foods – chopped *Tubifex*, sifted *Daphnia* and Grindal Worms.

FRY Size at: 7 days – 8 mm; 3 weeks – 11.5 mm; 1 month – 13 mm; 2 months – 20 mm. Adult coloration is reached in 8–9 weeks.

References and Further Reading

Castro, D. M. (1986) '*Corydoras gomezi*, a new species from Colombia (Pisces, Siluriformes, Callicthyidae)' *Boln Ectrop. Univ. Bogota* **15**: 33–8.

Castro, D. M. (1987) 'The freshwater fishes of the genus *Corydoras* from Colombia including two new species (Pisces, Siluriformes, Callichthyidae)' *Boln Ecotrop. Ecosist. Trop.* **16**: 23–58.

Fuller, I. A. M. (1978) '*Corydoras elegans* (Gold variety)' *C. A. G. B. Mag.* No. 17: 15–16.

Fuller, I. A. M. (1980) 'The first recorded spawning of *Corydoras barbatus*' *C. A. G. B. Mag.* No. 23: 19–22.

Fuller, I. A. M. (1981) 'Spawning *Corydoras amapaensis*' *C. A. G. B. Mag.* No. 31: 8–10.

Fuller, I. A. M. (1983) 'Look alikes unmasked' *Practical Fishkeeping* **1983** (Jan): 32–3.

Nijssen, H. (1970) 'Revision of the Surinam catfishes of the genus *Corydoras* Lacépède, 1803 (Pisces, Siluriformes, Callichthyidae)' *Beaufortia* **18**: 1–75.

Nijssen, H. (1971) 'Two new species and one new subspecies of the South American catfish genus *Corydoras* (Pisces, Siluriformes, Callichthyidae)' *Beaufortia* **18**.

Nijssen, H. & Isbrücker, I. J. H. (1970) 'The South American catfish genus *Brochis* Cope, 1872 (Pisces, Siluriformes, Callichthyidae)' *Beaufortia* **18**: 151–67.

Nijssen, H. & Isbrücker, I. J. H. (1976) 'The South American plated catfish genus *Aspidoras* R. Von Ihering, 1907, with descriptions of nine new species from Brazil' *Bijdr. Dierkunde* **46** (1): 107–31.

Nijssen, H. & Isbrücker, I. J. H. (1979) 'Chronological enumeration of nominal species and subspecies of *Corydoras*' *Bull. Zool. Mus. Univ. Amsterdam* **6** (17): 129–35.

Nijssen, H. & Isbrücker, I. J. H. (1980) 'A review of the genus *Corydoras* Lacépède, 1803. (Pisces, Siluriformes, Callichthyidae)' *Bull. Zool. Mus. Univ. Amsterdam*.

Nijssen, H. & Isbrücker, I. J. H. (1980a) '*Aspidoras virgulatus* n. sp. A plated catfish from Esperito Santo, Brazil (Pisces, Siluriformes, Callichthyidae)' *Bull. Zool. Mus. Univ. Amsterdam* **7**: 13.

Nijssen, H. & Isbrücker, I. J. H. (1980b) 'On the identity of *Corydoras nattereri* Steindachner 1877 with the description of a new species *Corydoras prionotos* (Pisces, Siluriformes, Callichthyidae)' *Beaufortia* **30**: 1–9.

Nijssen, H. & Isbrücker, I. J. H. (1980c) 'Three new *Corydoras* species from French Guiana and Brazil (Pisces, Siluriformes, Callichthyidae)' *Neth. J. Zool.* **30**: 494–503.

Nijssen, H. & Isbrücker, I. J. H. (1982) '*Corydoras boehlkei*. A new catfish from the Rio Caura system in Venezuela (Pisces, Siluriformes, Callichthyidae)' *Proc. Acad. Nat. Sci. Philad.* **134**: 139–42.

Nijssen, H. & Isbrücker, I. J. H. (1983) '*Brochis britskii*, a new species of plated catfish from the Upper Rio Paraguai system, Brazil. (Pisces, Siluriformes, Callichthyidae)' *Bull. Zool. Mus. Univ. Amsterdam* **9**: 20.

Nijssen, H. & Isbrücker, I. J. H. (1983a) 'Review of the genus *Corydoras* from Colombia with descriptions of two new species (Pisces, Siluriformes, Callichthyidae)' *Beaufortia* **33**: 53–71.

Nijssen, H. & Isbrücker, I. J. H. (1983b) 'Sept espèces nouvelles de poissons-chats cuirasses du genre *Corydoras*, Lacépède, 1803, de Guyana française, de Bolivie, d'Argentine, du Surinam et du Bresil (Pisces, Siluriformes, Callichthyidae)' *Rev. Fr. Aquariol. Herpetol.* **19**: 73–82.

Nijssen, H. & Isbrücker, I. J. H. (1986) 'Cinq espèces nouvelles de poissons-chats cuirasses du genre *Corydoras* Lacépède, 1803, du Perou et de l'Equateur (Pisces, Siluriformes, Callichthyidae)' *Rev. Fr. Aquariol. Herpetol.* **12**: 65–76.

Nijssen, H. & Isbrücker, I. J. H. (1986a) 'Review of the genus *Corydoras* from Peru and Ecuador (Pisces, Siluriformes, Callichthyidae)' *Stud. Neotrop. Fauna Envir.* **21** (1–2): 1–68.

Weitzman, S. J. (1954) 'A description, supplementary notes and a figure of *Corydoras cochui*, Myers and Weitzman, a Brazilian catfish' *Stanford Ichthyol. Bull.* **7** (4): 140–54.

Weitzman, S. H. (1961) 'Figures and descriptions of four South American catfishes of the genus *Corydoras*, including two new species' *Stanford Ichthyol. Bull.* **7**: 140–54.

Weitzman, S. H. & Nijssen, H. (1970) 'Four new species and one new subspecies of the catfish genus *Corydoras* from Ecuador, Colombia and Brazil (Pisces, Siluriformes, Callichthyidae)' *Beaufortia* **18**.

ADDENDUM

Since going to press, the following species have been described.

Corydoras breei
Isbrücker & Nijssen, 1992

Taxonomic Details
First collected in 1971 by M. Boesman.

ETYMOLOGY Named in honour of Dr Peter Jan Hendrik van Bree.

Distribution
Surinam: Avanavero Falls, Kabalebo River and Corantijn River system.

Description
SIZE The largest specimen examined was 39.9 mm, but this fish should grow to 50 mm in the aquarium.

Corydoras incolicana
Burgess, 1993

Taxonomic Details
First collected in 1992 by Adolfo Schwartz.

ETYMOLOGY From the Latin *incola* = 'an inhabitant' and Icana, the river from where it was found.

Distribution
Brazil: Rio Icana and Upper Rio Negro.

Description
SIZE The largest specimen examined was 50.6 mm, but this fish should grow to 60 mm in the aquarium.

Corydoras parallelus
Burgess, 1993

Taxonomic Details
First collected in 1992 by Adolfo Schwartz.

ETYMOLOGY Named because of the major colour feature – the parallel horizontal stripes on the sides.

Distribution
Brazil: Rio Icana and Upper Rio Negro.

Description
SIZE The largest specimen examined was 51.5 mm, but this fish should grow to 60 mm in the aquarium.

Corydoras virginiae
Burgess, 1993

Taxonomic Details
First collected in 1992 by Adolfo Schwartz.

ETYMOLOGY Named in honour of Adolfo Schwartz's wife, Virginia.

Distribution
Peru: Rio Ucayali.

Description
SIZE The largest specimen examined was 36.3 mm, but this fish should grow to 60 mm in the aquarium.

INDEX

Page references in italic refer to line drawings and in bold to colour plates.

CONVERSION TABLE

Length
1 mm	=	0.039 in
1 cm	=	0.394 in
1 m	=	3.281 ft

Area
1 cm^2	=	0.155 sq. in
1 m^2	=	1.196 sq. yd
1 ha	=	2.471 acre
1 km^2	=	0.386 sq. mile

Volume
1 cm^3	=	0.061 cu. in
1 m^3	=	1.308 cu. yd

Capacity
1 ml	=	0.035 fl. oz
1 l	=	{ 35.211 fl. oz 1.760 pt 0.220 gal

Note:

1 l	=	{ 2.113 US pt 0.264 US gal

Weight
1 g	=	0.0353 oz
1 kg	=	2.205 lb

Temperature
To convert °Centigrade to °Fahrenheit multiply by 9/5 and add 32.

Water Hardness
1°Clark	=	14.3 p.p.m. calcium carbonate
1°dH	=	17.9 p.p.m. calcium oxide

To convert °dH to °Clarke multiply by 0.56.